American Language Hub

LEVEL 2B
Workbook

with Key + access to Audio

CHRISTOPHER GOUGH

macmillan education

Macmillan Education Limited
4 Crinan Street
London N1 9XW

Companies and representatives throughout the world

American Language Hub Level 2B Workbook with Key
ISBN 978-1-380-04713-7
American Language Hub Level 2B Workbook with
Key + access to Audio ISBN 978-1-380-04707-6

Written by Christopher Gough

First published 2020

Original design by emc design ltd
Page make-up by SPi Global
Cover design based on an original design by Restless
Cover photograph by Getty Images/Linghe Zhao
Picture research by Emily Taylor

The authors and publishers would like to thank the following for permission to reproduce their photographs:

Alamy/BFA p51(tr), Alamy/Walter Bibikow p64(tr), Alamy/Urbanbuzz p63(tl); **Alan Tunnicliffe Photography** p65(owl); **BananaStock** p69(tr); **Corbis**/ Robert Marien p65(butterfly); **EyeEm**/Laura Vernocchi, p65(elephant); **Getty Images** pp65(gorilla, lion, moth, snake, tiger), 66, 71(Leo, Jason), Getty Images/AFP/Don Emmert p42(e), Getty Images/AFP/Tim Sloan p42(a), Getty Images/Veselina Alexandrova p63(br), Getty Images/Allsport Concepts Creative p69(tl), Getty Images/Anadolu Agency/Dursun Aydemir p53(Jolie), Getty Images/Blend Images pp47(1), 71(Yumi), Getty Images/Bloomberg/ JB Reed p54, Getty Images/Peter Cade p41, Getty Images/Canopy p52, Getty Images/Luiz Felipe Castro p67, Getty Images/Car Culture p57(bl), Getty Images/Cathy Crawford p63(tr), Getty Images/Creativ Studio Heinemann p40, Getty Images/Jake Curtis p45, Getty Images/Digital Zoo p65(toad), Getty Images/Dorling Kindersley p63(bl), Getty Images/EyeEm/Dori Arazi p44(Kites), Getty Images/EyeEm/Ronald Leunis p65(duck), Getty Images/EyeEm/ Gernot Molkenthin p65(alligator), Getty Images/FilmMagic/Bruce Glikas p53(Rowling), Getty Images/Foodpix/James Baigrie p63(bmr), Getty Images/ Hero Images p46, Getty Images/Zsolt Hlinka p72, Getty Images/Dave Hogan p42(c), Getty Images/Eric IsselÈe p65(panda), Getty Images/iStockphoto pp64(bl), 69(bl),74, Getty Images/iStockPhoto/Benimage p62(2), Getty Images/iStockPhoto/Grassetto p62(3), Getty Images/iStockPhoto/imtmphoto p43(br), Getty Images/iStockPhoto/lzf p43(bl), Getty Images/iStockPhoto/ LeeYiuTung p43(tr), Getty Images/iStockphoto/M_a_y_a p48, Getty Images/ iStockPhoto/Wacomka p47(5), Getty Images/Johner Images p57(br), Getty Images/Huw Jones p63(tml), Getty Images/Jutta Klee p61, Getty Images/ Krimzoya p47(3), Getty Images/Alex Livesey p42(d), Getty Images/LOOK p68, Getty Images/Linda Lyon p47(7), Getty Images/Maskot p71(Mohammed), Getty Images/Betsie van der Meer p55, Getty Images/Doug Menuez p69(br), Getty Images/Marvin E. Newman p44(Concorde), Getty Images/Popperfoto p44(Johnson), Getty Images/Graeme Purdy p47(2), Getty Images/Jenny E. Ross p60, Getty Images/Rundstedt B. Rovillos p65(ant), Getty Images/Serkan6 p47(4), Getty Images/Simonkr p70, Getty Images/Ariel Skelley p59, Getty Images/SueBurtonPhotography p62(1), Getty Images/Tetra Images p63(tmr), Getty Images/Time & Life Pictures p44(Earhart), Getty Images/UIG p44(Wright Brothers), Getty Images/UpperCut Images p56, Getty Images/VCG p53(tl), Getty Images/Duncan Walker p47(6), Getty Images/Wildestanimal p65(shark, tuna), Getty Images/WireImage/Samir Hussein p42(b), Getty Images/ WireImage/Dan MacMedan p53(tr); **iStockPhoto**/jtstewartphoto p65(eagle); **John Foxx Images** p65(fly, penguin); **Photodisc** p65(lizard); **Photospin** p65(parrot); **Rex Features**/Moviestore/Shutterstock p51(b); **Superstock** p44(tl); **Thinkstock Images** pp49, 50, 63(bml), 65(bear, bee), 65(crocodile, frog, monkey, mosquito).

Printed and bound in Uruguay

2022

2

Contents

GRAMMAR
Articles

A Use the prompts and add *the* / *a* / *an* to write complete sentences.

1 sun / rises / in / east.

____

2 president / of / US / lives in / White House.

____

3 is there / apple / in / shopping bag?

____

4 Tom / needs / to buy / new phone.

____

5 I'd like / to order / burger / without / fries.

____

B Choose the correct option to complete the text.

The Smiley Face

[1]*A / The / –* smiley face first appeared in 1963 when [2]*a / an / the* American children's TV show called *The Funny Company* featured it with the words 'Keep smiling' at the end of [3]*an / the / –* show.

In the same year, artist Harvey Ball designed something similar for [4]*a / the / –* local company. [5]*A / The / –* company used [6]*a / an / the* image to motivate its staff. Ball chose yellow for [7]*a / the / –* background because it was 'sunshiny and bright'.

However, it wasn't until 1970 that smiley faces became widely popular. Two brothers, Bernard and Murray Spain, produced [8]*a / the / –* button with [9]*a / the / –* classic smiley face and the words 'Have a nice day'. [10]*A / The / –* People loved it and, over the next two years, bought around 50 million buttons. Very soon, [11]*an / the / –* image appeared on [12]*a / the / –* huge range of products.

Today, hundreds of different smiley faces are used as [13]*an / the / –* emoticons or emojis in [14]*an / the / –* online messaging as a way of expressing emotions.

PRONUNCIATION
/ə/ (schwa) in *a* / *an*

7.1 **A** Listen and count how many articles (*a*, *an* or *the*) you hear in each sentence.

1 ___ 2 ___ 3 ___ 4 ___ 5 ___ 6 ___

7.1 **B** Listen again and repeat each sentence.

VOCABULARY
Feelings

A Complete each conversation with an adjective in the box.

anxious	cheerful	confused	glad
nervous	happy	relaxed	scared

1 **Marco:** Jenny's late. I'm surprised she hasn't called.
Kate: Yes, I'm starting to feel very ______________.

2 **Juan:** Are you less stressed after your vacation?
Ian: Yes, lying by a pool all day, I felt very ______________.

3 **Steve:** Is it a good time to talk to the boss?
Idris: Yes, he's very smiley and ______________ this morning.

4 **Mom:** How are you feeling about your exams?
Son: OK but I'm a little ______________ about them.

5 **Emma:** How's the new car?
Lara: We're very ______________ with it. It's much better than our old one.

6 **Terry:** What a nice present. You're so kind.
Eric: You're very welcome. I'm ______________ you like it.

7 **Julia:** Are you sure this is the right street?
Jorge: No, I'm a little ______________. All the streets look the same around here.

8 **Diana:** Why do you like sleeping with the light on?
Aisha: I'm ______________ of the dark.

B Complete each sentence below so that it is true for you.

1 I usually feel confused when I ______________
______________________________.

2 I usually wake up in a cheerful mood when ______
______________________________.

3 The last time I felt really nervous was when I
______________________________.

4 I was scared of ______________________
______________________ when I was little.

GRAMMAR
used to

A **Use the prompts to write full sentences using the correct form of *used to*.**

1. I / not / like / vegetables but now I do.
2. James / have / blue hair when he was a teenager.
3. you / play soccer together when you were kids?
4. the weather / not / be so cold in March.
5. Dave speaks French because he / live / in Paris.
6. people / really / go everywhere on horses?

B **Find and correct the mistakes in some of the sentences.**

1. I remember one day when my family used to go to the ocean for the day.
2. We used to be good friends.
3. I didn't used to listen to classical music.
4. Did Greg use to live next door to you?
5. She used to can stand on her hands.
6. What did you used to do after school on weekdays?
7. My dad used to have an old car that broke down all the time.

PRONUNCIATION
used to

7.2 **A** **Listen and write the sentences exactly as you hear them.**

1.
2.
3.
4.
5.
6.

7.2 **B** **Listen again and repeat the sentences.**

VOCABULARY
Shortened words

A **Use a shortened word of the word in bold.**

1. I'm not looking forward to being on the **airplane** for ten hours.
2. Can you help me carry my **suitcases**?
3. Jake's **cell phone** started ringing during the test.
4. The singer dropped the **microphone** and walked off the stage.
5. Stella sent me some **information** about the course.
6. Don't believe everything you read in the **newspaper**.
7. I only listened to the **introduction** to the radio show.
8. When did you work in the **laboratory**?
9. Does your company have a **website**?
10. We're allowed to use the **internet** to help with our homework.

B **Rewrite the shortened words in bold into the longer form.**

1. They took some really good **photos** in Miami.
2. My sister usually rides her **bike** to school.
3. I have an important **exam** tomorrow.
4. I have this great new **app** on my iPhone.
5. I'm not sure if it's true because I read it on the **net**.

GRAMMAR
No article (*school*, *the school*)

A For 1–7, complete each sentence with *the* or no article (–).

1 a The children aren't here. They're still at ___ school.
  b Peter's mother has gone to ___ school to speak to his teacher.
2 a The lawyer is in ___ prison speaking with one of his clients.
  b Marjorie's husband's in ___ prison. He robbed a bank.
3 a In the US, more people used to go to ___ church than they do now.
  b We went to ___ church in the city center to take some photos.
4 a Argh! There's a huge spider on ___ bed.
  b Is Mary still in ___ bed? It's 11 o'clock.
5 a John's at ___ hospital visiting his grandfather.
  b Jim's been in ___ hospital for two weeks with a chest infection.
6 a My aunt just got a job at ___ college.
  b Samantha just started at ___ college in Boston.
7 a The criminal will be in ___ court at the end of the month.
  b Hundreds of reporters were waiting outside ___ courthouse at the end of the trial.

B Find and correct the mistakes in some of the sentences.

1 Albert Einstein went to school in Munich.
____
2 Abraham Lincoln didn't go to the college.
____
3 Nelson Mandela spent 27 years in prison.
____
4 Katy Perry started her singing career in the church.
____
5 Naomi Campbell appeared in the court four times between 2000 and 2010.
____

VOCABULARY
Phrasal verbs

A Choose the correct option to complete the sentences (1–5). Then match each sentence to the correct picture (a–e).

1 He ***brought up*** / ***grew up*** in a poor part of Brazil but started playing for Santos when he was seventeen.
2 These two brothers formed the rock band Oasis. In the early 2000s, they had a ***falling out*** / ***dropped out*** and no longer see or speak to each other.
3 He ***dropped out*** / ***gave up*** of Harvard in 1975 after two years of study to found Microsoft.
4 She ***gave up*** / ***made up*** her acting career to marry a Royal Prince.
5 She ***made up*** / ***brought up*** her first *Harry Potter* story on a long train trip to London.

B Match each phrasal verb (1–6) with the list of nouns and phrases (a–f) that it collates with.

1 grow up
2 fall out with
3 bring somebody up
4 give up
5 make up
6 drop out of

a a story / a name / an excuse
b college / high school / society
c well / to be polite / with a love of books
d in the country / quickly / to be famous
e parents / brothers and sisters / a colleague
f a job / chocolate / trying

PRONUNCIATION
Practicing *the*: /ðiː/ or /ðə/

7.3 **A Listen and write *the* in the correct places in the text.**

University of Bologna is oldest university in world. It opened in year 1088 – a little earlier than University of Oxford, where teaching began in 1096. In Middle Ages, it was famous across Europe for study of law. Famous poet Dante studied there.

7.3 **B Listen again to check.**

READING

A PREDICT Look at the pictures. Predict what things make the people in the article happy.

B READ FOR MAIN IDEA Read the article quickly to check your predictions from Exercise A.

Glossary

company (n) being with other people
physically (adv) in a way that relates to your body
schedule (n) a plan of activities or events and when they will happen

C READ FOR DETAIL Read the article again. For questions (1–5), choose from people (a–d). You can choose each person more than once.

Who …

1 agrees with Jennifer that it is nice to spend time alone? ____
2 says that trying new things makes them happy? ____
3 thinks talking to someone close to you increases happiness? ____
4 believes that gaining knowledge is important for being happy? ____
5 says planning how they spent their time has made them happier? ____

D REFLECT Think about your answers to these questions.

1 Which person in the article do you most agree with?
2 What was the happiest day of your life?

The secret to happiness

For hundreds of years, great minds have argued over what makes us happy. We asked the people of Hong Kong to see if they had the answer.

a Ben, 24

For me, I never feel better than when I've set myself a challenge and then achieved it. It's not just that exercise makes us feel physically better; it's knowing that you did something today that you didn't yesterday. I like hiking in the hills and mountains around Hong Kong on my own. It takes me away from the pollution of the city below and gives me time to think.

b Jennifer, 33

When I moved to Hong Kong two years ago for work, I didn't know anyone. I was living by myself so I had to make friends quickly with colleagues and neighbors. After a few months, I was exhausted. I was going out for dinner or to a party almost every night. There was no 'me' time in my schedule. Now I make sure I have at least two nights a week at home with only a good book for company.

c Lin, 18

If I get good news, the first person I call is my best friend, June. Sharing my happiness makes me feel even happier. I've always liked to have company. I guess that's because I come from a big family and we socialize all the time. I don't mind if it's doing water sports or going to the movie theater; I just love to be surrounded by loved ones. I'm a real people person.

d Charlie, 41

I am an extremely curious person; some people would say I ask too many questions. For me, there would be nothing worse than doing the same thing day after day. What can you learn from that? This is why I've had so many different jobs over the years – teacher, tour guide, chef, the list goes on. I do the job for as long as I enjoy it; otherwise what's the point?

LISTENING

A PREDICT Can you name the people or things in the pictures?

B LISTEN FOR MAIN IDEA Listen to the radio show to check your predictions in Exercise A.
7.4

Glossary

disappearance (n) a situation in which someone or something can no longer be found or seen
historian (n) someone who studies or writes about events in history
major (adj) important, serious, large or great

C LISTEN FOR DETAIL Listen again. Number the events (a–h) in the order they happened (1–8).
7.4

___ **a** Richard Pearse successfully flies.
___ **b** First Concorde flight carrying people takes off.
___ **c** Leonardo da Vinci hides flight designs.
___ **d** Amy Johnson reaches Australia.
___ **e** People start flying kites.
___ **f** The radio show presenter flies on the Concorde.
___ **g** The first powered flight is recorded.
___ **h** Amelia Earhart goes missing.

D REFLECT Think about your answers to these questions.

1. Have you ever flown a plane? If not, would you like to?
2. How do you think flying will change in the future?

FUNCTIONAL LANGUAGE

Describe an object and say what you use it for

A Complete the conversations with the correct form of the verbs in the box.

call forgot know make think use (2x)

a **Customer:** Good morning. I'm looking for something, but I don't know what they're [1] ________.

Sales clerk: OK. Can you describe what you're looking for?

Customer: You [2] ________ them to put your wet clothes on a line to dry. They're [3] ________ of plastic or wood.

b **Matthew:** Hi, I wonder if you can help. I need something to make my shoes look nice – you know, shiny. Sorry, I can't [4] ________ of the word in English.

c **Luca:** Hi Ned, I need to borrow something, but I've [5] ________ the name of it in English.

Ned: A tool of some kind?

Luca: Yes, it's a thing you [6] ________ to cut wood. Do you [7] ________ what I mean?

B What objects do you think are being described in Exercise A?

WRITING

A Think about your answers to these questions.

1 What is your favorite subject now? What was your favorite subject ten years ago?

2 Do you think most people change what subjects they like to study as they get older?

B Look at the pie charts. What do they show? Do the results surprise you?

SUBJECT PREFERENCES OF 11- AND 18-YEAR-OLDS IN US PUBLIC SCHOOLS

Favorite subjects of 11-year-olds

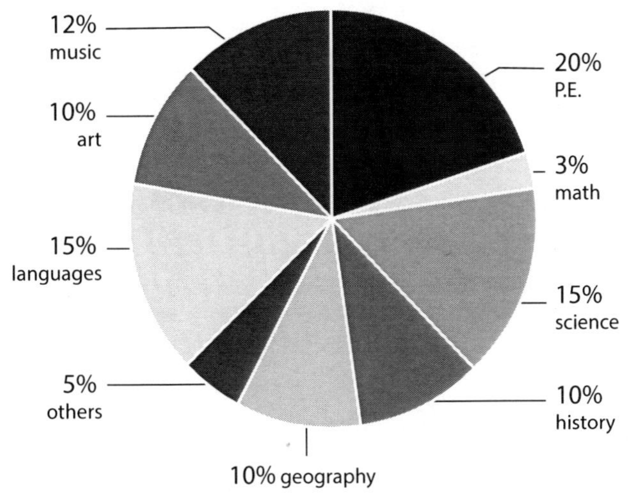

Favorite subjects of 18-year-olds

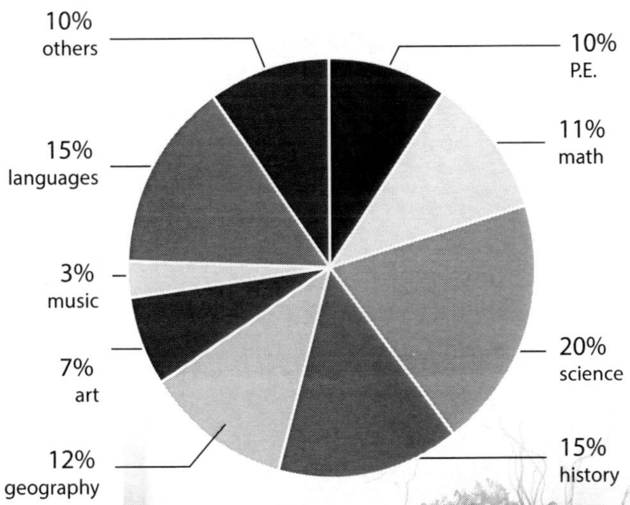

C Complete the survey report with words in the box.

according both comparison contrast lowest shows

The survey compared the favorite subjects of students at 11 years old with those at 18 years old. [1] ________ to the survey, students' preferences for most subjects changed over the eight years. The survey [2] ________ that P.E. is a favorite for 20% of the younger age group, but in [3] ________ only 10% of older students chose it. 12% of the younger group chose music as their favorite in [4] ________ to 3% of 18-year-olds. [5] ________ the 11-year-olds and 18-year-olds showed 15% choosing languages as their top subject. Math for the 11-year-olds and music for the 18-year-olds had the [6] ________ percentage of students choosing them as their favorite.

D Look at the survey report in Exercise C again and add two more sentences.

____

____

WRITING PRACTICE

A PREPARE You are going to write a survey report about people's favorite way to spend their free time. Look at the survey results conducted in a US city.

- Decide which of the data you will include.
- Decide how you can compare and contrast the data.
- Use the report in Writing Exercise C to help you.

How people like to spend their free time in Rochester, NY

Activity	18–30 years old	31 years old +
Socializing	60%	30%
Watching TV shows	5%	40%
Using social media	30%	20%
Working out	5%	10%

B WRITE Write your survey report using your notes from Exercise A.

GRAMMAR
Reflexive pronouns

A Match the sentence halves.

1 My brother and sister aren't speaking
2 Paul wouldn't help us
3 Please, come in
4 I didn't buy the cake,
5 Stop looking at

a so we had to clean up by **ourselves**.
b to **each other** right now.
c **yourself** in the mirror.
d I made it **myself**.
e and sit **yourselves** down.

B Complete the online post below with the correct reflexive pronoun.

When I was (almost) a rock star

I was in a band back in my college days. We taught [1] ______ to play our instruments. Jimmy, the guitarist, taught [2] ______ to play guitar, and Susie, the bass player, taught [3] ______ to play bass. I was the singer.

It wasn't really the music [4] ______ that mattered – we enjoyed thinking of [5] ______ as rock stars even before we had a good song!

I think a lot of people in bands take [6] ______ too seriously – I know we certainly did.

VOCABULARY
Music

A Choose the correct option in the sentences below.

1 She's a great *singer* / *guitarist*. I love her voice!
2 The *drummer* / *singer* has a really important part in the band; he or she keeps everyone in time.
3 He started playing the piano but then became a *keyboard player* / *guitarist*. They're very similar instruments.
4 He's not a *band member* / *drummer*, he just helps carry the equipment.
5 What is your favorite song on the *lyrics* / *album*?
6 I think good *lyrics* / *gigs* are important – they really help you understand the song's meaning.
7 They're going on *tour* / *cover songs* this September. I'm definitely buying a ticket!

B Complete the sentences with two of the words in each box. There is an extra word in each box that you do not need to use.

catchy cover live

1 There's a ______ of an old song that is being played on the radio a lot. It's very ______.

audience gig stage

2 When the band came on ______ the ______ went crazy.

live microphone stage

3 I don't know whether it was a problem with the ______ but she sounded terrible ______.

audience gigs show

4 It was one of the best ______ I've ever been to. The light ______ was amazing.

PRONUNCIATION
Consonant clusters in words

A Underline the consonant clusters in each word and try to say them.

1 strength
2 twelfth
3 sprints
4 splashed
5 screamed

8.1 **B** Listen and repeat the words.

VOCABULARY
Types of art

Complete the crossword using the picture clues (1–7).

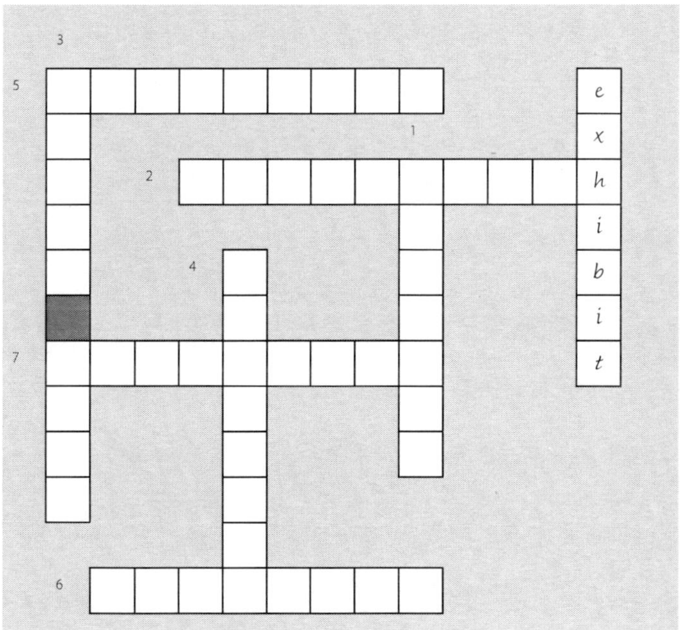

PRONUNCIATION
/ɪ/ and /iː/

A Decide if the vowel sounds in the first word and second word are the same (S) or different (D).

1 the big picture S / D
2 since three S / D
3 Did you leave? S / D
4 build a bridge S / D
5 weak lyrics S / D
6 visit the gym S / D
7 guitar king S / D
8 read music S / D

8.2 **B** Listen to check. Then repeat the phrases.

GRAMMAR
Infinitive of purpose

A Complete the sentences with the infinitive form of a verb in the box.

to avoid	to become	to create	to make	to see	to take

1 Some artists use unusual materials ______ their artwork.
2 We arrived at the exhibit early ______ the lines.
3 Artists mix red and yellow paint ______ orange paint.
4 Tourists visit the Louvre Museum ______ the *Mona Lisa*.
5 I bought a new camera ______ some photos at my brother's wedding.
6 Jill gave up her job ______ an artist.

B Reorder the words to form sentences.

1 bought / some wood / picture frame / make / I / to / a
______
2 went / Amsterdam / to / Jack and Sally / visit / the Van Gogh Museum / to
______
3 Zac / his girlfriend / some flowers / to / bought / surprise / her
______
4 the best / are / place / to / old movies / Small movie theaters / watch
______
5 homework / We / stayed up / to / our / finish
______

VOCABULARY
Movie and book genres

A Underline the movie or book genre described in sentences (1–6).

1. Tony likes really funny movies.
comedy / adventure / animated
2. Susan likes movies based on real people.
fairy tale / biopic / fantasy
3. Antonio's favorite book is about cowboys.
costume drama / Western / historical
4. Mary loves movies that scare her.
thriller / horror / action
5. Keira doesn't like movies set in space.
fantasy / sci-fi / fairy tale
6. Francesca finds all the singing annoying.
rom-com / biography / musical

B Complete the paragraph with the correct genre of book.

I've worked in a bookstore for the last five years. We used to sell a lot of [1] ________ and autobiographies because people were interested in the lives of famous athletes and celebrities a few years ago. Right now [2] ________ novels are very popular. I think people want to learn a little about the past while they read. [3] ________ is never unfashionable – I think these readers want to escape reality a little and discover an imaginary world! My favorite genre is [4] ________ – I like it when a lot of exciting things happen in books.

PRONUNCIATION
Word stress in longer words

A Underline the word stress in each pair of words below.

1	animated	animation	5	history	historical
2	adventure	adventurous	6	musical	musician
3	comedy	comedian	7	romance	romantic
4	fantasy	fantastic	8	science	scientist

8.3 **B** Listen to check.

GRAMMAR
First conditional

A Complete the conversation with the correct form of the verbs in parentheses. Use contractions where necessary.

Paolo: Hey Ana, do you want to go to the movie theater later?

Ana: Well, I [1] ________ (*go*) if there [2] ________ (*be*) something good playing.

Paolo: I like the look of this action movie with Bruce Willis.

Ana: It'll have too many fight scenes. If there [3] ________ (*be*) a lot of guns, I [4] ________ (*be*) bored.

Paolo: What about a comedy? [5] ________ you ________ (*go*), if we [6] ________ (*find*) a good rom-com?

Ana: Yes, I guess so. How are we getting there?

Paolo: If I [7] ________ (*drive*), it [8] ________ (*take*) a while to find a parking place.

Ana: That's OK. If we [9] ________ (*get*) there early, we [10] ________ (*have*) time to buy some popcorn.

B Choose the correct form in each sentence.

1. ***Will / Should*** we go out for dinner, if you don't feel like cooking?
2. If you see Olivia, ***could / should*** you tell her to call me?
3. We'll go to the exhibit if it ***is / will be*** free to get in.
4. Some people ***don't / won't*** swim in the ocean if they've just eaten.
5. If it's raining on Saturday, he ***might not / cannot*** come for a walk – he hasn't decided yet.

READING

A READ FOR MAIN IDEA Read the article quickly and choose the correct option in each statement.

1 The writer prefers seeing movies *at the movie theater* / *at home*.

2 The writer is *positive* / *not positive* about every part of going to the movie theater.

3 The writer says that going to the movie theater *is still very popular* / *has become unpopular*.

B READ FOR DETAIL Read the article again. Underline the *incorrect* option (a, b or c) in each sentence.

1 The writer thinks that buying a snack at the movie theater is …

a cheap.

b expensive.

c something most people enjoy.

2 The writer suggests that at the movie theater you might …

a not be able to see the screen clearly.

b have to listen to other people talking.

c not understand what's happening in the movie.

3 The writer claims that the money made from movies at the movie theater last year was …

a very good.

b disappointing.

c better than ever before.

4 The writer says that there has been great change to …

a the way movies are made.

b most forms of entertainment.

c the movie theater experience.

5 The writer uses the word *deafening* in the last paragraph to emphasize that …

a movies in movie theaters are loud.

b movie theaters are very dark.

c sound effects are very impressive.

6 The expression *a winning formula* in the last line is something …

a you don't understand well.

b that brings success.

c you shouldn't try to change.

C REFLECT Think about your answers to these questions.

1 Do you think people will continue going to the movie theater in the future, or will movie theaters have to change to keep attracting audiences?

2 Do you think movie theaters should be cheaper to encourage more people to go?

Glossary

3D (adj) three dimensional

comfort (n) state of feeling comfortable

row (n) a series of people or things arranged in a straight line

Why Do We Still Love the Big Screen?

These days, we can stream and download movies on a widescreen high-definition television in the comfort of our own living room. Why then do we still go the movie theater?

At most movie theaters, the cost of a soda and bag of popcorn is higher than in a store and almost the same as the cost of downloading a movie. And, as we all know, a visit to the movie theater usually means sitting behind someone who blocks your view or next to someone who can't stop whispering to a friend about what's happening.

However, the public is more passionate than ever about the big screen. Last year, the money taken in at movie theaters across the world hit an all-time high of around $35 billion. In the US alone, the figure was nearly $15 billion. So, what's the explanation?

I think we love the movie theater because it hasn't changed. There have been huge advances in making movies but a trip to the local movie theater is the same as it always was. While other forms of entertainment have transformed or been forgotten, the movie theater is the same as it was 60 years ago and that's something people can trust.

People just love sitting in rows in a dark theater gripped by the giant image and deafening sound effects. What's more, they want to share the experience with as many people as possible. Buying popcorn in the lobby is old-fashioned but familiar. Going to the movie theater is safe and predictable and everyone's happy. Why change a winning formula?

LISTENING

A PREDICT Look at the picture of graffiti/street art. You will hear a father (F) and daughter (D) discussing it. Choose who you think will make each point below.

1. There is no difference between graffiti and street art. *F / D*
2. Having art on walls is better than having nothing on walls in the city center. *F / D*
3. It is important that creative young people can exhibit their art. *F / D*
4. Street art makes it seem that people don't care about their environment. *F / D*
5. It is expensive to clean graffiti off buildings. *F / D*
6. Banksy's art is interesting. *F / D*

8.4 **B LISTEN FOR SPECIFIC INFORMATION** Listen to the conversation and check your answers to Exercise A.

Glossary

engaging (adj) attractive and pleasant in the way that makes people like something
to show off (phrase) to behave in a way that is intended to attract people's attention and make them admire you
valuable (adj) worth a lot of money

8.4 **C IDENTIFY CONTRAST** Listen again and complete the sentences with the words or phrases in the box.

although another important difference but compared to though

1. Especially ____________ a few years ago.
2. … it has really changed around there, ____________ when you say graffiti …
3. I'd prefer nice clean white walls ____________.
4. I agree, ____________ that's not the same thing.
5. … his work is engaging and, ____________, extremely valuable.

D REFLECT Think about your answers to these questions.

1. Do you agree more with the father or more with the daughter?
2. Is there much street art in your hometown or city?

FUNCTIONAL LANGUAGE

Show interest in a topic

8.5 **A** Match the sentence halves. Then listen to check.

believe kidding real too way

1. The gig has been canceled.
2. The tickets cost $100 each.
3. Look, that's Chris Martin over by the bar.
4. I love this song they're playing.
5. This song's number one right now.

a. No ____________! He's just someone who looks like him!
b. I don't ____________ it. It's terrible.
c. For ____________? You must have more money than sense.
d. Oh no, you're ____________! I was really looking forward to it.
e. Yeah, me ____________! It's so catchy.

B Complete the conversations with the correct form of *be* or *do*.

1. **Jessica:** I love that movie.
   Gareth: Yes, so ____________ I.
2. **Sean:** I didn't enjoy the movie much.
   Alik: No, neither ____________ I.
3. **Louise:** Jenny's found a job as a music producer.
   Oliver: She ____________? That's awesome.
4. **Ryan:** I really like heavy metal.
   Liam: You ____________? It just gives me a headache.
5. **Bella:** I have tickets for the Reading Festival this year.
   Harry: So ____________ I. We can go up together.
6. **Will:** Tim and Liz are having a party this weekend.
   Fred: They ____________? That should be really fun.

WRITING

A Think about the answers to these questions.

1. What is the purpose of a book or movie review?
2. Do you ever read reviews before you read a book or watch a movie?
3. Would you still go to see a movie if the review was negative?

B Read the review. Is the review positive or negative?

C Read the review again. In which paragraph (a–c) are the following mentioned?

1. the plot or story ______
2. when the movie is set ______
3. writer's opinion of the movie ______
4. writer's opinion of the actors ______
5. writer's recommendation ______
6. the genre ______

D Complete the review with the correct form of one of the verbs in the box.

see	be	set	star	tell

WRITING PRACTICE

A PREPARE Write notes on each of the points below.

- Choose a movie you have seen that is based on a book.
- Write down the title, genre, theme and main characters.
- Think about the main points of the plot.
- Make a note of what you liked or didn't like about it.
- Think about whether you would recommend it.

B WRITE Write your review in 100 words. Use your notes and ideas from Exercise A.

C REVIEW Remember to check your writing for spelling, grammar and punctuation mistakes.

Success strikes again

a *Murder on the Orient Express* is a classic mystery novel by Agatha Christie. It [1]______ the story of world-famous detective Hercule Poirot deciding which of the twelve suspects is guilty as the train travels from Istanbul to London.

b It [2]______ Kenneth Branagh, Penélope Cruz, Judi Dench and many more famous actors. The acting [3]______ excellent. It's [4]______ in the 1930s and the costumes are incredible.

c The movie is even more exciting and engaging than the book because there are more action scenes. If you like mysteries, it's definitely worth [5]______.

PRONUNCIATION
/ɑː/, /ʌ/ and /æ/

9.1 **A Listen to the phrases below. Decide if the vowel sounds in the first and second word are the same (S) or different (D).**

1 last chance S / D
2 after lunch S / D
3 after dark S / D
4 much cash S / D
5 love money S / D
6 bad man S / D
7 bad luck S / D
8 pass back S / D
9 done once S / D
10 can't run S / D

9.2 **B Say the words aloud and <u>underline</u> the one with a different vowel sound. Then listen to check.**

1 month / come / sun / half
2 done / path / shut / blood
3 fat / black / because / grammar
4 stand / ask / bath / fast
5 other / laugh / enough / stuff
6 ham / calm / lamb / ram

GRAMMAR
Second conditional

A Complete the text with the correct form of the verb in parentheses. Use contractions where possible.

Sometimes I wish I was still in college. My life then was a lot of fun compared to now. If I [1] ______ (*be*) still in college, I [2] ______ (*not have to*) get up at 6:30 every morning and I [3] ______ (*not spend*) an hour standing on a crowded train. If I [4] ______ (*can*) go back to college, I [5] ______ (*go*) right now.

I suppose if I [6] ______ (*not have*) a job, I [7] ______ (*not be earning*) any money, but, who knows, if I [8] ______ (*not do*) this boring job, I [9] ______ (*might*) an actor, a rock singer or a soccer player.

B Complete each question with the correct form of a verb in the box.

buy can go have offer say see share tell win

1 If you ______ spend $2000 on a single article of clothing, what ______ you ______?
2 ______ you ______ somebody if you ______ a person leave a grocery store without paying?
3 What ______ you ______ if a company ______ you a lot of money to work in Australia for three years?
4 ______ you ______ your money with your friends if you ______ the lottery?
5 If you ______ the ability to travel in time, which year ______ you ______ back to?

VOCABULARY
Prepositions in money phrases

Complete the article with words in the box. Use verbs in blanks (1–7) and prepositions in blanks (a–i).

borrow by for from in lend on out of pay pay save spend take to toward up

Attitudes [a] ______ money have not changed in the US in the past few years. Families still [1] ______ most of their money [b] ______ food and housing.

Many people still [2] ______ money [c] ______ family members rather than go to the bank. Statistics show that parents who [3] ______ money [d] ______ sons and daughters usually do not expect to be paid back.

You can [4] ______ [e] ______ products and services [f] ______ debit or credit card these days. However, some people would still rather [5] ______ money [g] ______ of the ATM and [6] ______ [h] ______ cash.

The most common things that people [7] ______ [i] ______ for are a house and their retirement.

VOCABULARY
Verbs connected with money

Match the sentence halves.

1 JK Rowling has given away
2 Chinese multibillionaire Jack Ma made
3 Actress Angelina Jolie supports
4 Did you know Leonardo DiCaprio and Kate Winslet donated
5 Do you think movie stars earn
6 The singer owed
7 The soccer player lost
8 The TV announcer raised

a $20 million, which he couldn't afford to pay back.
b so much money, she's no longer a billionaire.
c more than $400,000 to a young mother?
d money for a children's charity by dancing non-stop for 24 hours.
e too much money?
f a lot of money from the technology industry.
g all of his money because he bought too many expensive things.
h at least 30 charities from all over the world.

PRONUNCIATION
/s/and /z/

9.3 **A** Listen and underline the word you hear. Then practice saying both words.

1 peas / peace
2 race / raise
3 raced / raised
4 racer / razor
5 bus / buzz
6 ice / eyes
7 plays / place
8 sink / zinc

9.4 **B** Listen to the way the /s/ and /z/ sounds merge together in the phrases below. Then practice saying the phrases.

1 please sit
2 his suit
3 fizz sticks
4 lose sleep
5 he's sorry
6 kiss Zac
7 his story
8 Julie's zig-zag skirt

GRAMMAR
Essential adjective clauses

A Match the words (1–7) with their definitions (a–g). Then use the correct relative pronoun to complete each definition.

1 A donor
2 A donation
3 'Black Friday'
4 A vault
5 A beggar
6 An inheritance
7 A materialist

a is an amount of money or property ________ somebody receives when a family member dies.
b is a secure room ________ banks store money, gold or other valuables.
c is somebody ________ donates money to charities and good causes.
d is a gift or an amount of money ________ somebody gives away.
e is a person ________ life revolves around money and possessions.
f is a day each year ________ people can buy a lot of things more cheaply.
g is a person ________ asks people for money on the street.

B Complete the second sentence so that it has a similar meaning to the first sentence. Use four or five words.

1 Your mother and I got married here.
This is ________________ got married.
2 That guy lives next door to Peter.
There's the ________________ to Peter.
3 Most people travel to and from work during the rush hour.
Rush hour is the time ________________ to and from work.
4 Shakespeare was born in this city.
This is ________________ was born.
5 I would really hate to lose my cell phone.
My cell phone is one thing ________________ to lose.

GRAMMAR
Gerunds

Complete the text using the correct form of a verb in the box.

call collect create hire make realize shop sign

The story of eBay

Pierre Omidyar started *AuctionWeb* in 1995 without [1] ________ that it would become one of the most successful websites in history. He knew that [2] ________ online was a growing business, and he had the idea of [3] ________ a site for people to sell items to whoever offered the most money. At first, it was a hobby and [4] ________ a lot of money was not Omidyar's plan.

One of the first items to be sold was a broken laser pointer at $14.83. The buyer told Omidyar that he loved [5] ________ old office items, especially broken laser pointers!

Soon, thousands of people started [6] ________ up which resulted in Omidyar [7] ________ his first employee.

In 1997, the company wanted to change its name to *EchoBay* but the name was already taken. [8] ________ the company eBay was always a second choice, but it is now a familiar name to almost everyone in the world.

VOCABULARY
make and *do* expressions

A Put the phrases in the correct column.

a complaint a decision a living a mess a mistake an offer a profit me a favor research some damage the ironing the shopping your homework

make	do

B Complete the conversations using the correct form of an expression from Exercise A.

1 **Wife:** Oh dear, we don't have any bread.
Husband: Don't worry, I'm going to ________ later.

2 **Tina:** I bought two tickets for $60 and then sold them online for $80.
Lola: So, you've ________ of $20.

3 **Son:** Can I watch TV?
Dad: Well, only if you ________ first. It's math, isn't it?

4 **Daughter:** I'm going to paint some pictures in the kitchen.
Mom: OK, but don't ________; I've just cleaned it.

5 **Lorenzo:** The hotel was awful.
Tai: Have you ________? You might get some money back.

6 **Customer:** I thought you said the bill was for $35.
Waiter: Sorry, I ________. It's $45.

PRONUNCIATION
/ʒ/ and /dʒ/

A Underline the words with a /ʒ/ sound. Circle the words with a /dʒ/ sound.

angel average damage decision image inclusion leisure massage orange pleasure region religion television

B Listen to check your answers in Exercise A. 9.5

READING

A PREDICT Read the title of the article. Which statement (a–d) do you think will be the best summary for the article?

- **a** The article will tell people what it is like to be a student with no money.
- **b** The article will give students advice about money.
- **c** The article will advise students about how to look good without spending a lot of money.
- **d** The article will advise students about where to buy the best designer clothes.

B Read the article to check your prediction from Exercise A.

C READ FOR MAIN IDEA Read the article again quickly and match the headings (a–d) to each paragraph in the text (1–4).

- **a** Buy used clothing
- **b** Recycle what you have
- **c** Shop online
- **d** Go to markets

D SCAN Read the article again focusing on the highlighted words. Use the context to choose the correct option in each definition below.

1. **Breaking the bank** *is a type of crime / means spending all your money at once.*
2. In paragraph 1, **wardrobe** means *a large piece of furniture for clothes / all the clothes you possess.*
3. **Delivery** is *bringing products to your home / what products are packed in.*
4. **Shop around** means *compare prices in various places / go to a real store rather than buying online.*
5. **Browsing** means *calculating amounts of money / looking at various options without buying.*
6. A **stand** is *a small store that is open at the front / a person who is good at selling things.*
7. **Rock-bottom** means very *high / low.*
8. A **bargain** is something you pay *more / less* than you expected to.
9. In paragraph 7, **dresser** means *a large piece of furniture for clothes / all the clothes you possess.*

E REFLECT Underline two pieces of advice in the article that you agree with.

Glossary

headscarf (n) article of clothing worn around the head, usually by women
snakeskin (adj) made from the skin of a snake – usually boots, coats and handbags
vintage/classic (adj) old but of very high quality / special to a specific time in the past

Dress for Less on a Student Budget

You might not be able to afford designer clothes and the very latest accessories, but you still want to look good. We're here to give some tips on how to be cool without **breaking the bank**. Remember that it's style that's important – not how much your **wardrobe** costs.

1 ______________________

This is a great way of saving money and time. There are almost always sales going on and many stores offer free **delivery**. You can find the best deals without leaving the comfort of your bedroom.

Prices vary on different sites, so **shop around** and be prepared to spend time **browsing** and bookmarking pages. Shop on auction sites like eBay. They're known for some unusual items but there's plenty of regular clothing, too.

2 ______________________

Shop at outdoor markets that are held at the same location. You'll find all sorts of **stands** selling clothing and accessories. Prices will be lower than in stores and can usually barter if you think something's too much.

3 ______________________

Every town has charity stores where you'll find clothes and accessories that people have donated. Prices are **rock-bottom**, and you will occasionally find genuine **bargains** such as a vintage coat or a classic handbag for just a few dollars.

Remember that the cash you spend in these stores helps people in need and that recycling of any kind is good for the planet.

4 ______________________

Before you even think about shopping, check your **dresser** – or your mom and dad's! An old concert T-shirt might look supercool on you and one of your mom's headscarves might make a great skirt.

And, finally, share with friends. If your roommate wants to borrow your pink sweater for the evening, borrow her snakeskin jacket in exchange. You'll both look great without spending a penny.

LISTENING

A PREDICT You are going to hear a radio show about shopping. Look at the picture and predict the topic (a–c).

- **a** Different ways of shopping
- **b** Stores closing because of online shopping
- **c** How stores can keep their customers

9.6 **B** Listen and check your idea from Exercise A.

Glossary

publicity (n) attention in magazines, online, newspapers or television

retailer (n) a business or person who sells things to the public

9.6 **C LISTEN FOR MAIN IDEA** Listen again. Are the sentences true (T) or false (F)? Correct the false sentences.

1. Stores are now making more money than in the past. *T / F*
2. Online sites cost less to manage than a store. *T / F*
3. In real stores, customers don't usually like to talk to sales clerks. *T / F*
4. People always go to stores because they want to buy something. *T / F*
5. Customers usually like to hold and touch a product. *T / F*
6. People like to see businesses supporting local events. *T / F*
7. Retail businesses don't need to be online at all. *T / F*
8. Positive comments left online aren't always good for business. *T / F*

D REFLECT Think about your answers to these questions.

1. Do you prefer shopping online or going into a store?
2. Do you like asking sales clerks for advice, or do you prefer making decisions alone?
3. In the future, do you think everyone will do all their shopping online?

FUNCTIONAL LANGUAGE

Go shopping for clothes and ask for a refund

9.7 Listen and complete the conversations using one word in each blank.

1

Sales Person: Can I [1]_________ you?

Customer: Yes, I'm [2]_________ for accessories – something for my wife's birthday.

Sales Person: What kind of [3]_________ are you looking for – gloves, a belt, some jewelry?

Customer: Gloves are a good idea.

Sales Person: The gloves are [4]_________ there, sir. Let me know if you need help.

Customer: I like these. I'll [5]_________ them.

Sales Person: Very well, sir. That's $25. How would you like to [6]_________?

Customer: By card, here.

Sales Person: OK, if you could [7]_________ your PIN when you're ready.

Customer: OK.

Sales Person: Thank you, sir. Would you like them [8]_________-wrapped?

Customer: No, don't [9]_________. I'll do that when I get home.

2

Customer: Hello, I bought this T-shirt yesterday but it's the [10]_________ size. It's a little big.

Sales Person: Would you like to [11]_________ it for a smaller one?

Customer: Actually, I'd prefer to have a [12]_________ if that's OK. I'm not sure I like it that much.

Sales Person: OK, I can do that if you have the [13]_________.

Customer: Yes, here it is. Thanks so much for that.

WRITING

A Match the sentence halves to complete advice for writing 'for sale' ads.

1 You must get the buyers' attention so
2 Start with what is special about the item, for example,
3 If it has a definite price,
4 Make the buyer take action;
5 If needed, include the specifications,

a its condition, price or accessories.
b keep it short and simple.
c such as speed and size.
d use words like 'only'.
e give them your contact information to get further details.

B Read the ads. Find and correct the ten mistakes.

C Look at the ads. Do they follow the advice? Underline examples of 1–6.

1 best or key features
2 how good the price is
3 specification
4 accessories
5 condition
6 contacting the seller

WRITING PRACTICE

A PREPARE Write answers to the following questions.

1 Which of your possessions would you like to sell?

2 How much would you sell it for?

3 What condition is it in?

B WRITE Write your 'for sale' ad in 30–50 words.

- Use your answers and ideas from Exercise A.
- Use the advice in Writing Exercise A.

C REVIEW Remember to check your writing for spelling, grammar and punctuation mistakes.

VOCABULARY
Electronic devices

Match the problems (1–6) to the device in the box that could help.

drone e-reader fitness tracker
power bank tablet USB drive

1 Rachael has to write reports while she's traveling. ________

2 Mike's a photographer and he's traveling in Thailand soon. He wants to shoot a video from up high. ________

3 Jill needs to save some huge files but there's no space on her laptop. ________

4 Lisa takes four paperbacks on vacation, but she's fed up of carrying them in her luggage. ________

5 Tim's phone is always running out of battery when there's nowhere to plug it in to recharge. ________

6 Margot's trying to lose weight and keep track of how much exercise she does. ________

GRAMMAR
Comparatives and superlatives

A Complete the paragraph with the comparative or superlative form of the adjective in parentheses.

I've just bought a new computer and I can't believe how much [1]________ (*fast*) it is than my old one. It's definitely [2]________ (*good*) purchase I've made this year. My old machine was almost ten years old, and it just got slower and [3]________ (*slow*). When I turn the new computer on, everything happens so much [4]________ (*quick*) than it did with my old computer. The old one took much [5]________ (*long*) to warm up.

[6]________ (*bad*) thing about the old computer was the fuzzy screen. It used to give me a headache. The new screen is [7]________ (*wide*) than the old one and that's [8]________ (*kind*) to my eyes.

The new computer was [9]________ (*expensive*) than I was expecting so I saved some money. I don't usually buy [10]________ (*modern*) devices but I'm glad I bought something up to date this time.

All in all, it's much [11]________ (*reliable*) and I'm much [12]________ (*happy*) with it.

B Look at pictures a and b and find eight differences. Write comparative sentences using the adjectives in the box.

beautiful big comfortable
high long modern old tall

1 ________
2 ________
3 ________
4 ________
5 ________
6 ________
7 ________
8 ________

a

b

PRONUNCIATION
/ɪst/ and superlative adjectives

10.1 **Listen and count how many superlative adjectives you hear in each sentence.**

1 ___ 2 ___ 3 ___ 4 ___ 5 ___ 6 ___

VOCABULARY
Using devices and the internet

Choose the correct verb to complete the sentences.

1 I couldn't *remember / block* my password and I had to contact the website to reset it.
2 Could you show where to *make / connect* the USB drive on your laptop?
3 I *installed / clicked* on a link and all sorts of warnings appeared on the screen.
4 The screen *froze / crashed* and I had to call somebody in to fix the problem.
5 I usually *make / connect* a video call to my family in Australia just to say 'Hi'.
6 He entered the wrong password three times and the site *crashed / blocked* his account.
7 Most people save a copy of important files on a USB drive in case their computer *remembers / crashes*.
8 Josie *installs / clicks* all the latest apps as soon as they're available.

PRONUNCIATION
/əz/ in comparative structures

10.2 Listen and complete the sentences.

1 Jimmy isn't ______ he looks.
2 Taking the train is ______ flying.
3 I'm doing it ______ I can.
4 You can take ______ you like.
5 It didn't cost ______ we were expecting.
6 Taking care of the kids all day is ______ going to work.

GRAMMAR
More comparative structures

A Find and correct the mistakes in some of the sentences.

1 Your cell phone isn't as better as mine.
______
2 The movie wasn't as good like I expected.
______
3 London is as expensive as New York.
______
4 Online banking is as safer as it needs to be.
______
5 Joe doesn't earn as much money than his wife.
______
6 My 12-year-old daughter can read as well as I can.
______
7 Messi isn't playing as good as usual.
______
8 Now that we have children, we don't go out as regularly as we would like to.
______

B Rewrite the second sentence so it has a similar meaning to the first. Use *not as … as* or *just as … as*.

1 Normal bank accounts are safer than online bank accounts.
Online bank accounts are ______ normal bank accounts.
2 I thought Tim's new house would be bigger.
Tim's new house is ______ I thought it would be.
3 Tony is no better or worse at chess than his younger brother.
Tony's younger brother is ______ he is.
4 Jenny is smarter than all her brothers.
Jenny's brothers are ______ she is.
5 Tony and Steve ate the same amount as Debbie.
Tony and Steve ate ______ Debbie.

GRAMMAR

need to

A Complete each sentence using the correct form of *need to* and an appropriate verb.

1 To be an elementary school teacher, you ________ patience.

2 An accountant ________ good with numbers.

3 To work as a taxi driver, you ________ the local area very well.

4 To be an artist, you ________ a good imagination.

5 Business people in London ________ German, but it is very useful.

B Reorder the words to make questions.

1 you / do / exercise / do / to / more / need / ?

____

2 does / to / need / she / English / learn / ?

____

3 you / see / do / need / doctor / to / a / ?

____

4 he / more / need / borrow / money / to / does / ?

____

PRONUNCIATION

/ʊ/ and /uː/

10.3 **A** Decide if the vowel sounds in the first word and second word are the same (S) or different (D). Then listen to check.

1 look good	___	5 I would move	___
2 good food	___	6 a good cook	___
3 too soon	___	7 a full pool	___
4 a few books	___	8 a rude woman	___

B Say the words in each list below aloud and underline the word with the different vowel sound.

1 tooth / look / moon / shoot	4 rude / put / suit / crew
2 took / soon / good / foot	5 should / wood / loose / full
3 stood / true / you / rude	6 knew / could / shoes / use

10.4 **C** Listen to check your answers to Exercise B.

VOCABULARY

Collocations: science and research

A Complete the sentences below with the correct form of a verb in the box.

collect do do follow look for make repair solve test

1 Scientists are always ________ research on the effects of climate change.

2 That man is responsible for ________ laboratory equipment when it is not working properly.

3 The team ________ several important discoveries at a site in Cornwall. One coin could be over a thousand years old.

4 My diet is very strict. I have to ________ the same schedule every day, starting at 7:00 am.

5 Computer companies spend millions of dollars ________ new technologies before they start selling them.

6 The role of a customer service department is to deal with customers and ________ any problems they are having.

7 I've spent a month ________ a solution to this problem.

8 There are organizations that ________ and share the data of every internet user in the country.

9 We need to ________ more experiments before we make a conclusion.

B Underline the noun in each list that is not used with the verb.

1 **make** *preparations / a discovery / research*

2 **test** *new technology / experiments / problems*

3 **look for** *schedule / a solution / answers*

4 **do** *research / experiments / data*

Technology and the Traveler

a Like everyone else, I love my technology. However, when I'm traveling it's different. I understand how technology can affect the experience. I want to escape day-to-day life, not be connected to it every minute of the day.

b I remember traveling twenty years ago. At a typical hostel, groups of backpackers gathered in groups. Some played cards or chess, but most just sat around exchanging stories about the difficulties and problems they had while they traveled. I used to arrive and make friends really quickly.

c Now, young travelers sit in silence, each updating family and friends with news and photos on their social media sites. If I want to start a conversation with one of them, I have to drag him or her away from their devices. They're more interested in the latest episode of *Game of Thrones* than talking to me. Travelers used to share their travel experience with those having the same experience. Now, they prefer to share it with their mom and dad or best friend two thousand miles away.

d Of course, technology brings benefits. I used to spend hours in banks exchanging travelers' checks. Now, I go to an ATM and get my money in seconds. I remember losing my friend in Mexico. We were miles from our hostel and wasted a day trying to find each other. Now, a quick text and we would reunite immediately.

e I guess it's all about balance. Reserving your hotel in advance is convenient, but arriving in a city with nowhere to stay can be exciting. Knowing exactly where everything is and how long it'll take to walk there makes you feel in control, but takes away a sense of adventure. Getting lost opens your eyes, and might result in an experience you didn't expect.

f So when traveling, spend half an hour calling home or checking your emails but then turn all the technology off and look around you. You're surrounded by new and exciting things ... you're not going to discover them on social media!

Glossary

drag (v) pull somebody
reunite (v) bring together again after separation
sense of adventure (phrase) wanting to do new and exciting things

READING

A PREDICT Read the title of the webpage. What examples of technology do you think will be in the article?

B Read the article quickly to check your predictions in Exercise A.

C READ FOR MAIN IDEA Read the article again. In which paragraph (a–f) does the writer make points (1–5)?

1 Some things were more difficult without modern technology. ___
2 Young travelers used to enjoy each other's company. ___
3 Modern technology has both advantages and disadvantages. ___, ___ and ___
4 He doesn't want to be always in contact with people back home. ___
5 It is difficult to get to know strangers these days. ___

D READ FOR SPECIFIC INFORMATION Read carefully and complete the sentences below with one word from the article.

1 Travelers used to spend time telling each other ________.
2 The writer used to make ________ easily when he traveled.
3 Today, travelers are more likely to spend time ________ their social media.
4 The writer says that ATMs and text messaging are both ________ of modern technology.
5 It is sometimes more ________ not to have everything carefully planned.

E READ FOR DETAIL Identify each sentence from the text below as fact (F) or opinion (O).

1 At a typical hostel, groups of backpackers gathered in groups. ___
2 I used to spend hours in banks exchanging travelers' checks. ___
3 Arriving in a city with nowhere to stay can be exciting. ___
4 Getting lost opens your eyes. ___
5 You're surrounded by new and exciting things. ___

F REFLECT Do you use technology more or less than usual when you travel?

1

2

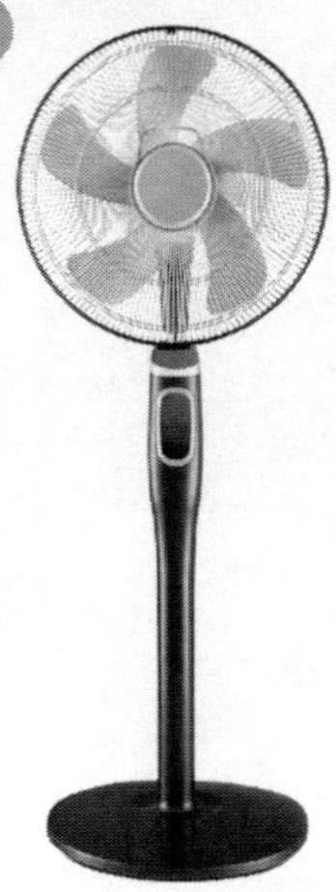

3

LISTENING

A PREDICT Match the pictures (1–3) to the words in the box.

electric fan | microwave | mobility scooter

10.5 **B LISTEN FOR MAIN IDEA** You are going to listen to three conversations.
In which conversation (1–3) is a speaker …

a on vacation? ___ **b** shopping? ___ **c** at home? ___

Glossary

two nights in a row (phrase) two nights following one after another

vehicle (n) a machine that you travel in or on, especially one with an engine that travels on roads, for example, a car, bus, van, truck or motorcycle

10.5 **C LISTEN FOR DETAIL** Listen to the three conversations again. Then complete the exercises.

Conversation 1

Who makes each point below? Underline man (M) or woman (W).

1. A microwave means needing to cook less. M / W
2. A microwave can mean that you cook less than you should. M / W
3. A microwave makes life easier. M / W
4. Cooking in a microwave might not be totally safe. M / W

Conversation 2

Answer the questions.

5. Who is the customer going to buy the mobility scooter for? ___
6. How much is the one the customer is looking at? ___
7. What is the fastest speed it can go? ___
8. Why doesn't the customer want it? ___

Conversation 3

Decide if statements (9–13) are true (T) or false (F).

9. The woman expected air-conditioning in the apartment. T / F
10. The woman looked for a fan in the apartment. T / F
11. The apartment owner offers to bring a fan immediately. T / F
12. The woman is happy with one fan. T / F
13. The woman will get the fan eventually. T / F

D REFLECT What appliance could you not live without?

FUNCTIONAL LANGUAGE

Make and receive formal and informal phone calls

10.6 Complete each phone conversation with a word in the box. Then listen to check.

back | breaking | busy | gone | hear | hold | possible | put | signal | up

1

Jenny: Hello, Cartwright's. Jenny speaking, how can I help you?

Susanna: Oh, hello. Is it [1] ___ to speak to Mr. Jenner, please?

Jenny: I'm not sure. I'll just try to [2] ___ you through. No, I'm afraid his line's [3] ___. Would you like to [4] ___?

Susanna: Actually, I'm very busy myself. I'll call [5] ___ later.

2

Tina: Hi … hi Matt … hi is that you?

Matt: Oh, hi Tina. Yes, it's me but I can't [6] ___ you very clearly. Could you speak [7] ___?

Tina: Can you hear me now? I'm at Grand Central …

Matt: Sorry, you've [8] ___ again. *I'll* try to call *you*. Hi Tina, is that better?

Tina: Not really, it's a terrible line. You keep [9] ___ up.

Matt: Well, I'm just collecting the car. I'm in an underground parking garage. The [10] ___ isn't very good.

Tina: Why didn't you tell me that? Call me again when you're outside.

10.6 Science and Technology

Write a recommendation

Hey! I'm moving into a student house next month. It's a new house and there's nothing in there! We're going to buy furniture, but what electrical devices do I need to buy? We don't have a lot of money so we can't buy too many things. Thanks for your help!

Elsa

Hello Elsa! Hmm, I think you should definitely buy a dishwasher. When you share with other students, it will stop you from arguing about whose turn it is to do the dishes. Think about getting one that isn't too expensive to use and is a reliable brand. You don't want it to keep breaking! Also, I'd recommend getting one that is fairly powerful, so your dishes get really clean.

I'd also suggest getting a washing machine. I know there are places you can take your laundry, but it's much more convenient to have a washing machine in your house. I'd recommend getting a fairly large one so you can wash a lot of clothes at once. I'd suggest getting one that's quiet so it doesn't disturb other people in the house.

A microwave was never as useful as I thought it would be when I was a student. I actually liked cooking fresh meals for my friends so we hardly ever used it. One thing that is very useful for the kitchen is a kettle, since most students I know drink a lot of tea and coffee. Or if your budget is big enough, you could buy a coffee machine – they make great fresh coffee in an instant!

Hope that helps!

Marcus

WRITING

A Look at the pictures. Which three things do you think would be most useful when moving into your first home?

B Read Elsa's question on an online message board. Then read the response from Marcus. Did he recommend the same three things you thought of in Exercise A?

C Read Marcus' response again and underline the structures he uses to make recommendations.

WRITING PRACTICE

A **PREPARE** Read the three questions from an online message board. Choose one which you would like to answer.

1 I don't know whether to buy a fitness tracker or join a gym. I want to get in shape quickly and need some motivation! What should I do?

2 Should I take a job that is well-paid but far away from my friends and family or one with a low salary that is closer to home?

3 I don't know whether to buy an old car or a new bicycle. I travel 5 km to work every day so I need something reliable. Can anyone help me decide?

B **PLAN** Write notes on what recommendations you'd make. Think about which structures from Writing Exercise C you could use.

C **WRITE** Write your recommendation in 100 words.

VOCABULARY
Natural features

A Find fifteen natural features in the word search.

U	Y	S	F	F	I	L	C	D	D	O
L	A	N	A	C	A	N	Y	O	N	C
Y	E	L	L	A	V	A	J	Q	B	E
A	L	I	G	H	T	S	L	N	A	A
M	O	U	N	T	A	I	N	H	Y	N
R	A	I	N	F	O	R	E	S	T	S
L	E	E	H	A	R	B	O	R	R	F
N	V	O	N	A	C	L	O	V	K	E
W	A	T	E	R	F	A	L	L	T	E
U	C	L	S	T	R	E	S	E	D	R

B Put the words you found in Exercise A in the correct column in the table.

Land	Water	Others

PRONUNCIATION
/e/ and /iː/

11.1 Listen and underline the word you hear.

1 meat / met
2 beast / best
3 feed / fed
4 feel / fell
5 mean / men
6 cheek / check
7 seed / said
8 cleaver / clever

GRAMMAR
The passive voice (simple present and simple past)

A Complete the text with the correct passive form of a verb in the box.

attract cover create erode know locate make reach

Table Mountain [1] ________ in the heart of Cape Town in South Africa. During its formation 250 million years ago, the layer of soft rock at the top [2] ________ by the wind and rain. However, the main part of the mountain, which [3] ________ of much stronger rock, stayed. This gave the mountain its unusual flat top.

More than a million people visit Table Mountain each year. They [4] ________ by the spectacular views over the city. There are several walking routes up the mountain but the top can also [5] ________ by cable car. The mountain is usually [6] ________ by thick cloud, which [7] ________ as the 'table cloth'.

B Complete the text with the active or passive form of the verbs in parentheses.

Frequently, the Taj Mahal [1] ________ (*describe*) as the most beautiful building in the world. One thing that [2] ________ (*impress*) visitors is the way the gardens [3] ________ (*design*) to be exactly the same on each side. This [4] ________ (*give*) the palace a beautiful sense of symmetry. The whole building [5] ________ (*reflect*) in a huge pool, while smaller pools and fountains [6] ________ (*create*) a feeling of calm.

The Taj Mahal [7] ________ (*build*) for Shah Jahan, one of the most important men in India. In 1629, his favorite wife suddenly [8] ________ (*die*) and the Shah [9] ________ (*fill*) with sadness. To remember her, he decided to construct the most beautiful monument imaginable.

GRAMMAR
Adjective + infinitive

Complete the text below with an adjective from the first box in (1–5) and an infinitive verb from the second box in (a–e).

dangerous disappointed easy impossible lucky

to drive to get to go to hear to see

Last year, my wife and I went on our first safari. We stayed in a great location and it was [1]______ [a]______ to the savanna and forest. On the first day, we were [2]______ [b]______ that we couldn't go and see any animals because bad weather was expected. We were told that if it rained heavily, it would be [3]______ [c]______ the jeeps along the dirt so we spent the day by the swimming pool instead. The second day was much brighter. It wasn't long before we came across a herd of elephants at a drinking hole. We were told we shouldn't get out of the car because it would be [4]______ [d]______ too close – the elephants might charge at us. Later in the day, we saw lions and rhinoceros. The guides said we were [5]______ [e]______ rhinos on our second day since they are very rare.

VOCABULARY
Animals

Write the names of the animals in the pictures above in the correct column in the table . The first letters have been given to help you.

Mammals	Birds	Insects
b______	e______	a______
e______	d______	b______
g______	o______	b______
l______	p______	f______
m______	p______	m______
p______		m______
t______		

Reptiles	Amphibians	Fish
a______	f______	s______
c______	t______	t______
l______		
s______		

PRONUNCIATION
to /tə/

11.2 Listen and count the number of words you hear in each sentence. Contractions count as two words.

1 ___ 3 ___ 5 ___ 7 ___

2 ___ 4 ___ 6 ___ 8 ___

PRONUNCIATION

/l/ pronounced and silent

11.3 **A** Listen and check (✓) the words in which the *l* is pronounced.

cloud	☐	plastic	☐
would	☐	family	☐
palm	☐	reptile	☐
fail	☐	lake	☐
laugh	☐	half	☐
should	☐	climate	☐
trail	☐	left	☐
calm	☐		

11.3 **B** Listen again and repeat the words.

GRAMMAR

even

A Find and correct the mistakes in some of the sentences.

1 We have a lot of pets at home. Even we have a lizard.

____

2 The animals in that zoo seem so unhappy. The monkeys even look sad.

____

3 Joan won't throw anything away. She even keeps her old toothbrushes.

____

4 It was a wonderful party. My grandmother was even dancing.

____

5 They have very few electrical appliances. They don't have even a TV.

____

6 Jason was an hour late and didn't even apologize.

____

7 The most remote places on Earth even are polluted.

____

8 Even Martin said the dish looked delicious and he's a vegetarian.

____

B Write *even* into the correct place in each sentence.

1 This beach is so dirty – the locals leave their trash here.
2 They don't use the car they have.
3 My boyfriend got me Coldplay tickets. I don't like Coldplay.
4 It's a really easy book – my little sister can read it.
5 Craig eats too much fast food. He eats burgers for breakfast.

VOCABULARY

somewhere, nowhere, everywhere, anywhere

A Complete the conversations with *somewhere*, *nowhere*, *everywhere* or *anywhere*.

1 **A:** Do you have a problem with graffiti in your town?
B: Yes, it's _______________.
2 **A:** I can't find my passport.
B: It must be _______________.
3 **A:** Where are you going Jinny?
B: _______________ exciting. I just need to mail some letters.
4 **A:** Where should I sit?
B: _______________ you like. I don't mind.
5 **A:** Where should we go on vacation this year?
B: As long as it's _______________ hot I don't mind.
6 **A:** Is Lee Adam's best friend?
B: Yes, they go _______________ together.
7 **A:** Where do you want to go out to eat later?
B: _______________ too expensive. I don't have much money.

B Complete the second sentence so it has a similar meaning to the first. Use *somewhere*, *nowhere*, *everywhere* or *anywhere* and two other words.

1 I've spent the morning looking for my glasses, but I can't find them.
I can't find _______________.
2 These days, Japanese restaurants are on every street.
These days, you can find _______________.
3 I want to take my girlfriend to a really nice restaurant for her birthday.
I want to take my girlfriend _______________ for her birthday.
4 Parking in the city is impossible.
There's _______________ in the city.
5 It doesn't matter where you look, there's trash.
There's trash _______________.
6 All the hotels are booked. I don't know where we'll stay.
There isn't _______________.

READING

A PREDICT Think about possible answers to these questions.

1 Which two countries is Niagara Falls in?

2 How high is Niagara Falls?

3 How many people visit each year?

B Read the first paragraph of the article to check your predictions from Exercise A.

C READ FOR DETAIL Answer the questions.

1 Why do so many people visit Niagara Falls every year?

2 Why is the American side of the falls less popular with tourists?

3 What has been the effect of less tourism for the American side?

4 What is the reason for the large number of gift shops on the Canadian side?

5 Why is the writer angry that people were taking photographs at the falls?

D REFLECT Think about your answers to these questions.

1 Have you ever been disappointed by a popular tourist attraction?

2 Do you think having a high number of tourists can ever be a good thing?

Are tourists destroying the world?

Niagara Falls, on the border between Canada and the US, is a magnificent natural wonder. It is 53 meters high and a massive 670 meters wide. All of which have made it one of the most popular tourist destinations in the world. Over 30 million people visit every year and the number of visitors is likely to increase.

The American side of the falls is not as impressive as the Canadian side. As a result, it is rarely visited and because of this it hasn't changed too much over the years. However, the Canadian side of the falls could not be more different. The huge number of tourists means that there is money to be made. This has led to many gift shops and museums selling poor-quality souvenirs around the area and overpriced restaurants serving terrible food are everywhere.

When I visited last March, I was so disappointed. Most of the time all that I could see were people taking selfies with the falls in the background. This means that no one seemed to appreciate the amazing natural beauty right in front of them. It was not at all what I'd imagined.

Next year, I'm going on a trip up the Amazon River through the rainforest. Hopefully in the middle of nowhere, I will be safe from people posing with their phones.

Glossary

appreciate (v) to see and understand what is good or special about a person or place
impressive (adj) very good or very large
massive (adj) very large

LISTENING

A PREDICT Read the extract below and answer the questions.

Suddenly, we saw this huge cloud of dust in the distance. It was a brown-yellow color. It was clearly coming our way.

1 Where do you think the people are?

____

2 What do you think was coming their way?

____

11.4 **B LISTEN FOR MAIN IDEA** Listen to a man telling his friend about something that happened to him. Check your answers from Exercise A.

Glossary

dust (n) very small pieces of dry earth or sand that are like powder

stick (v) to become fixed to something, especially by means of a sticky substance

11.4 **C LISTEN FOR DETAIL** Listen to the story again. Are the sentences true (T) or false (F)? Correct the false sentences.

1 The speaker went into the desert to work. *T/F*

2 He didn't know there was going to be a storm. *T/F*

3 His local colleagues quickly understood what was happening. *T/F*

4 The wind made it hard for him to move quickly. *T/F*

5 Some of his colleagues took off their shirts because it was hot. *T/F*

6 The speaker was angry about getting his clothes dirty. *T/F*

D REFLECT Think about your answers to these questions.

1 Have you ever heard a similar story? What happened?

2 Have you ever been in a situation where you were helped by local people?

FUNCTIONAL LANGUAGE

Tell a story

A Complete the sentences with the correct word.

1 Did I _______________ tell you about what happened when I was in Libya?

2 Why? What _______________?

3 It _______________ really scary. What happened _______________?

4 Oh _______________? Did you get back to the truck safely in the _______________?

11.5 **B** Listen to check your answers.

11.6 Natural World

Write an email giving suggestions and advice

WRITING

A Look at the pictures and think about the questions below.

1. Have you ever moved somewhere new and needed to make friends?
2. What is a good way to meet a lot of people?

B Read Michelle's email to her cousin Becky and her response. Do you agree with Becky's advice?

TO: Becky

FROM: Michelle

SUBJECT: Any tips?

Hello Becky,

How are things? I'm so nervous about starting at a different college next month. Everyone there knows each other already and I'll be the only new person. Do you have any advice?

Thanks,
Michelle

TO: Michelle

FROM: Becky

SUBJECT: RE: Any tips?

Hey Michelle!

First of all, it's important not to worry too much. I'm really confident and even I was nervous in my first week, so it's completely normal.

If I [1] __________ you, I would join a few clubs and societies. You're good at sports, so why not try to get on a team? It's a good [2] __________ to try a few different things so you meet different types of people. Maybe you could join a drama or musical group too.

Make [3] __________ you smile and talk to people when you can. Going out is a [4] __________ – you can't meet new people if you sit in your bedroom all day.

Finally, you [5] __________ suggest studying together with people in your classes. It's a good way to connect to people while getting your work done.

I hope that helps!

Becky

C Complete Becky's email with the words in the box.

idea	must	should	sure	were

D Correct the mistakes.

1. You really ought go out every evening.
   ____
2. I recommend telling to your teacher.
   ____
3. He really must to visit the gallery when he's there.
   ____
4. I'd suggest you to take the bus.
   ____

WRITING PRACTICE

A PREPARE Imagine your friend is starting a new job or college and he/she is feeling nervous. Write down three or four pieces of advice you would give him/her.

B WRITE Write your email in 100–150 words. Use your ideas from Exercise A.

VOCABULARY
News expressions

A Match each word or phrase in the box to its meaning (1–7).

breaking news · follow the news · get the news · journalist · news headlines · report the news · share news stories

1 watch the news ______
2 pay attention to the news ______
3 communicate the news ______
4 the very latest news ______
5 a person who writes about the news ______
6 repost reports on social media ______
7 biggest news stories ______

B Complete the sentences with the correct form of the words or phrases in Exercise A.

1 He doesn't have time to ______ closely, so he just listens to the ______.
2 She ______ from an app on her phone. She usually ______ about health and fitness.
3 They both want to be ______ and go out of the country to ______ from different countries.
4 To be honest I only watch it if there's important ______.

GRAMMAR
Reported speech

A Rewrite the direct speech as reported speech.

1 'I love posting photos of myself.'
Joanna said that ______.
2 'Bill do you know the way to the movie theater'?
Ian asked ______.
3 'I'll see you tomorrow.'
Sally told ______.
4 'Should I hand in my homework now'?
Roberto asked ______.
5 'Daniel is watching the soccer game tonight.'
Helena said that ______.

B Find mistakes in some of the sentences. Then rewrite the incorrect sentences.

1 My students asked me where was I going on vacation.
______
2 Phil told Sarah that he liked her shoes.
______
3 Lionel told that he couldn't answer my question.
______
4 James said us that he didn't like sports much.
______
5 Samantha told me she's forty-two a couple of months ago.
______

PRONUNCIATION
/ɒ/, /ɔː/ and /oʊ/

A (12.1) Listen to the phrases below. Decide if the vowel sounds in the first and second word are the same (S) or different (D).

1 go home	S / D		6 four frogs	S / D
2 more boxes	S / D		7 hope so	S / D
3 short story	S / D		8 short walk	S / D
4 lost phone	S / D		9 both doors	S / D
5 what song?	S / D		10 know more	S / D

B (12.2) Listen and <u>underline</u> the word with the different vowel sound.

1 top / what / lost / talk
2 sport / caught / comb / door
3 bone / bored / road / local
4 stop / clothes / wrong / wasp
5 thought / caught / cough / clock
6 cloth / though / both / pros

VOCABULARY
Television

Complete the text with a word/phrase in the box. Sometimes more than one word is possible.

box set | channels | episode | show | season | season finale | series | stream

Forgot about switching 1 ______ or waiting weeks for the 2 ______ so you can finally find out how the 3 ______ ends. Buy the *TV Choice* app to 4 ______ your favorite 5 ______ or download a single 6 ______. We also have the full 7 ______ of your favorite 8 ______ from the past. Join today and get $10 off!

PRONUNCIATION
Word stress in past perfect sentences

12.3 **A** **Listen and underline the phrase you hear in each pair below.**

1 you lost / you'd lost
2 the movie started / the movie had started
3 I heard about it / I'd heard about it
4 we found it / we'd found it
5 they played well / they'd played well
6 Mom cooked / Mom had cooked

12.3 **B** **Listen again and repeat.**

GRAMMAR
Past perfect

A **Use the simple past or past perfect form of the verbs in parentheses.**

1 The wolf ______ (*be*) very hungry because he ______ (*not eat*) all day.
2 I ______ (*not understand*) the story because I ______ (*miss*) the first episode of the series.
3 The movie ______ already ______ (*start*) when we ______ (*arrive*) at the movie theater.
4 I ______ (*recognize*) one of the students because I ______ (*teach*) her in Milan the year before.
5 Jamie ______ (*thank*) his father for all the help he ______ (*give*) him.
6 June ______ never ______ (*taste*) lychees before so she ______ (*be*) surprised by their sweetness.
7 My hair ______ (*be*) really dirty when I got back from camping. I ______ (*not take*) a shower for three days.
8 Jack ______ (*cannot*) find his car keys and then realized he ______ (*leave*) them on the table in his hotel room.

B **Look at the pictures below. Read the story and put the people in the order that they arrived at the office.**

Leo arrived in the office a few minutes after Jason. He'd followed him from the subway station. When Jason got there, Yumi had already arrived. Jason had come to work earlier than usual because he hadn't written a report and he hoped to do it before the boss appeared.

Yumi had arrived at the office ten minutes earlier than Jason. She'd had an idea during the night and wanted to start working on it.

However, Mohammed, the boss, had arrived before everyone. He'd only come so early because his wife needed the car for an important meeting and had dropped him at the office on her way.

1 ______
2 ______
3 ______
4 ______

Jason

Leo

Mohammed

Yumi

GRAMMAR
should

A Complete the sentences using *will* or *should*. Use contractions where possible.

1. That new yogurt looks delicious. ________ I get some when I go shopping later?
2. ________ we invite Adam to come out later? I know he's free this evening.
3. **Benny:** Can I get you a drink?
   Maria: OK, thanks. I ________ get the next round.
4. Here, use some of my sunscreen. You ________ get burned in this heat.
5. **Sara:** I don't know if I should take this job or not.
   Eddie: Well, ________ I tell you what I think?
6. Dinner is almost ready. ________ you set the table for me?
7. Don't worry, they ________ be here soon.
8. **Mike:** Jim and Katie are late, aren't they?
   Alice: ________ I text them and find out where they are?

B Complete the second sentence so it has a similar meaning to the first. Use *will* or *should* and two other words.

1. Let's go to the movie theater later.
   ________ to the movie theater later?
2. I'd like some help with these bags.
   ________ me with these bags?
3. Tina is going to pass her test.
   ________ her test for sure.
4. Who do you want to invite to our party?
   Who ________ to our party?

VOCABULARY
Advertising

Complete each text extract below with a word or phrase in the box.

brand catch your eye connect with grab your attention logo message slogan

1. The goal of all advertising is to ________. Nobody is going to buy a product if they don't know anything about it.
2. TV advertisements usually feature beautiful people because advertisers want to send out a ________ that using the product makes the user attractive to other people.
3. A lot of people feel that wearing a fashionable or expensive ________ of jeans tells other people that they are successful.
4. Occasionally, a ________ like McDonalds' *I'm lovin' it!* becomes so well known that people use it in everyday conversation.
5. Slogans should be short and memorable so that they ________.
6. Advertisers know that people will ________ a message that makes them feel they are making a sensible choice.
7. Most big soccer clubs make money from wearing a company ________ on the team shirts.

PRONUNCIATION
/æ/ and /e/

12.4 Listen and underline the word you hear. Then practice saying both words.

1	bad	bed	5	sad	said
2	had	head	6	dad	dead
3	man	men	7	mat	met
4	sand	send	8	gas	guess

READING

A PREDICT Look at the links below from an online news homepage. Think of one kind of report you might find if you clicked on each one.

Education Entertainment Finance Lifestyle News Headlines Sports Travel Weather

B READ FOR MAIN IDEA Match each of the headings in Exercise A with a news story found on the right.

C READ FOR DETAIL Answer the questions below about each extract.

1 Does the weather report give very bad or fairly good news?

______

2 Is the Entertainment extract serious news or gossip?

______

3 Is the Lifestyle news about family life or health?

______

4 Which sport is the Sports extract about?

______

5 Does the Finance extract give good or bad news?

______

D READ FOR SPECIFIC INFORMATION Look at the numbers below and think about what they refer to in the text. Then read the text to check.

1 24 ______
2 10% ______
3 60% ______
4 ninth ______
5 three ______
6 $28 million ______

E REFLECT Think about your answers to these questions.

1 What are the breaking stories in your country today?
2 Do you prefer reading serious news or celebrity gossip?

Glossary

blame (v) to say or think that someone or something is responsible for an accident, problem or bad situation

election (n) an occasion when people vote for someone to represent them, especially in a government

fog (n) a thick cloud that forms close to the ground or to water and is difficult to see through

rumor (n) unofficial information that may or may not be true

1 ______

Rain and snow in high areas will clear toward the end of the day, leaving only the far northwest cold and windy. Tomorrow will be around 24 degrees, mainly dry with sunny spells. Some fog can be expected early on Tuesday.

2 ______

According to scientists, most adults eat more than they need to every day. Many people are not sure how many calories they need and even fewer count the number. To help, a new diet plan called *Count With Us* has been launched.

3 ______

Actress Emma Langley and business tycoon Claude Monreal were photographed walking hand-in-hand again last night. This comes two days after the couple was seen having dinner at the Ivy restaurant in Soho. Fans are certain this confirms rumors that the pair are dating.

4 ______

Parents in the UK are less likely to spend time helping their children with homework than parents in almost any other country. Just 10% of UK moms and dads help children with school work every day. That is far behind India, where 60% of parents lend a hand.

5 ______

We are still awaiting the final election news but we will update you as the results come in.

6 ______

Not long ago, spending the night at an airport hotel was very dull. We immediately thought of uncomfortable beds and bad food. Now, however, excellent airport hotels are opening everywhere. Here are ten to keep an eye out for …

7 ______

Max Hemmings kept his World Heavyweight title last night when he beat Mexican Juan Herito on points. Herito was knocked down in the 9th round but recovered to last until the final bell. Hemmings has won all three of his fights this year.

8 ______

AbbeyWide lost almost $28 million in 2017 after making a profit of $14 million in 2016. The company is blaming the economic crisis.

LISTENING

A PREDICT You will hear two people arguing about the pros and cons of allowing children to watch TV. Write down at least one argument for each point of view.

12.5 **B LISTEN FOR MAIN IDEA** Listen and answer the questions.

1 Why are the couple discussing the topic at this particular time?

____

2 Do either of them mention the arguments you thought of in Exercise A?

____

12.5 **C LISTEN FOR DETAIL** Listen again and decide whether Erica (E) or Tony (T) makes each point below.

1 Tony's nephew and niece watch a lot of TV. ___
2 They only watch a lot of TV when there are visitors. ___
3 Children should get plenty of exercise. ___
4 Watching TV makes children think. ___
5 TV is not the only way to watch shows. ___
6 A TV brings a family together in one place. ___
7 TV can entertain a baby when parents are busy. ___
8 The amount of TV parents allow their children to watch gradually increases. ___
9 Parents should teach children how to do things. ___

D REFLECT Think about your answer to these questions.

Who do you agree with, Erica or Tony?

Were you allowed to watch a lot of TV as a child?

FUNCTIONAL LANGUAGE

Give and respond to opinions

A The sentences below are from the recording. Complete each with one word in each space.

1 Oh _______________! Sally lets them watch a little more TV than usual when …
2 Yes, of _______________, most of the time.
3 That's not _______________. Most shows …
4 Well, sorry, but I _______________
5 Look, all I'm _______________ is let's have no TV while the baby's small.
6 Now, that's my point _______________! One minute you say …
7 Well, yes … maybe that's a _______________ point.
8 Well, I'm not _______________ about that but let's say …

12.6 **B** Listen to check your answers.

WRITING

A Look at the picture and read the story. Then answer the questions.

1 Do you know the whole story well?

____

2 How is the story here different from the usual version?

____

B Complete the story with the correct form of the verb in parentheses. Use simple past, past progressive and past perfect.

C Read the story again and circle three examples of reported speech and underline one example of direct speech.

WRITING PRACTICE

A **PREPARE** You are going to write a similar news story based on a fairy tale, fable or well-known story. Choose from the headlines below or invent a headline of your own.

Prince Charming Finds His Mystery Girl (end of story in this lesson)

Dwarves Heartbroken After Girl Guest Bites Poisonous Apple

Terrified Girl Escapes House of Bears

Tortoise Beats Proud Hare in Forest Race

- Choose a story you know very well.
- Decide whether it is best to tell just part of the story. All of the story might be too much.

B **WRITE** Write your story in 100–150 words using your ideas from Exercise A.

Mystery Girl Leaves Slipper at Royal Ball

A beautiful girl has apparently stolen Prince Charming's heart. The mysterious young woman danced with the prince all evening but then suddenly [1] __________ (*disappear*) into the night.

Rich and famous guests from across the kingdom [2] __________ (*receive*) invitations to last night's ball. They [3] __________ (*dance*) and enjoying themselves, when the girl appeared in a long blue gown and glass slippers. Nobody [4] __________ (*see*) her before and they were amazed at her beauty. One man said she was the prettiest girl he had ever seen.

It [5] __________ (*not take*) the prince long to spot the mystery guest and soon they were dancing cheek to cheek. The prince's aunt told us that she [6] __________ (*not see*) her nephew so happy for many years and that he clearly [7] __________ (*fall*) madly in love.

Then, suddenly, as the clock struck midnight, the girl [8] __________ (*rush*) out. As she raced down the palace steps, she lost one of her slippers. As the prince and his men [9] __________ (*chase*) the girl, they found the slipper she [10] __________ (*drop*).

Now the prince has promised to find the beautiful girl. He told us he would search the entire kingdom and that he would not stop until they were reunited. 'If I have to try the slipper on the foot of every girl in the land, then I will do it', he said.

Irregular Verbs

Base form	Past simple	Past participle
be	was/were	been
become	became	become
begin	began	begun
break	broke	broken
bring	brought	brought
build	built	built
buy	bought	bought
can	could	(been able to)
catch	caught	caught
choose	chose	chosen
come	came	come
cost	cost	cost
cut	cut	cut
do	did	done
drink	drank	drunk
eat	ate	eaten
fall	fell	fallen
feel	felt	felt
find	found	found
forget	forgot	forgotten
get	got	got
give	gave	given
go	went	gone/been
grow	grew	grown
have	had	had
hear	heard	heard
hit	hit	hit
hold	held	held
hurt	hurt	hurt
keep	kept	kept
know	knew	known
leave	left	left
lend	lent	lent

Base form	Past simple	Past participle
let	let	let
lose	lost	lost
make	made	made
mean	meant	meant
meet	met	met
must	had to	(had to)
pay	paid	paid
put	put	put
read	read	read
ride	rode	ridden
run	ran	run
say	said	said
see	saw	seen
sell	sold	sold
set	set	set
shut	shut	shut
sing	sang	sung
sit	sat	sat
sleep	slept	slept
speak	spoke	spoken
spell	spelled	spelled
spend	spent	spent
stand	stood	stood
steal	stole	stolen
take	took	taken
teach	taught	taught
tell	told	told
think	thought	thought
throw	threw	thrown
understand	understood	understood
wear	wore	worn
win	won	won
write	wrote	written

PHONETIC SYMBOLS											
Single vowels			Diphthongs			Consonants					
/ɪ/	fish	/fɪʃ/	/ɪə/	ear	/ɪə/	/p/	pen	/pen/	/s/	snake	/sneɪk/
/iː/	bean	/biːn/	/eɪ/	face	/feɪs/	/b/	bag	/bæg/	/z/	zoo	/zuː/
/ʊ/	foot	/fʊt/	/ʊə/	tourist	/'tʊərɪst/	/t/	tea	/tiː/	/ʃ/	shop	/ʃɒp/
/uː/	shoe	/ʃuː/	/ɔɪ/	boy	/bɔɪ/	/d/	dog	/dɒg/	/ʒ/	television	/'telɪvɪʒən/
/e/	egg	/eg/	/əʊ/	nose	/nəʊz/	/ʧ/	chip	/ʧɪp/	/m/	map	/mæp/
/ə/	mother	/'mʌðə/	/ju/	use	/juz/	/ʤ/	jazz	/ʤæz/	/n/	name	/neɪm/
/ɜː/	word	/wɜːd/	/aɪ/	eye	/aɪ/	/k/	cake	/keɪk/	/ŋ/	ring	/rɪŋ/
/ɔː/	talk	/tɔːk/	/aʊ/	mouth	/maʊθ/	/g/	girl	/gɜːl/	/h/	house	/haʊs/
/æ/	back	/bæk/				/f/	film	/fɪlm/	/l/	leg	/leg/
/ʌ/	bus	/bʌs/				/v/	verb	/vɜːb/	/r/	road	/rəʊd/
/ɑː/	arm	/ɑːm/				/θ/	thing	/θɪŋ/	/w/	want	/wɒnt/
/ɒ/	top	/tɒp/				/ð/	these	/ðiːz/	/j/	yes	/jes/

UNIT 7

7.4 Lesson 7.5, Listening, Exercise B
J = John K = Kate

J: Today, we are learning about the history of flying with historian Dr. Kate Young. Kate, surely the history of airplanes isn't that long. The Wright Brothers were the first to fly a plane in 1903, weren't they?

K: A powered plane yes, and soon after in 1904, Richard Pearse also managed to leave the ground for a few seconds. But long before that, between 1485 and 1500, Leonardo da Vinci designed *flying machines*. He kept his drawings hidden, therefore they weren't discovered until long after his death some 400 years later.

J: That's incredible.

K: Well, humans have always dreamed of flying. Long before passenger flight was possible and even much earlier than Da Vinci, in fact over 2000 years ago, people in China were making kites.

J: Wow, I never knew that.

K: But you are right to say that most of the major events in flying happened during the 20th century. One of the most well-known events was the disappearance of Amelia Earhart in 1937 while she was flying over the Pacific. Previously, in 1932, she became the first woman to fly solo across the Atlantic.

J: I thought Amy Johnson was the first person to fly across the Atlantic.

K: No, just before Earhart in 1930, Amy Johnson flew from England to Australia.

J: Oh yes, I always get those two confused since they were around at the same time.

K: Another important date is 1976, the first passenger flight of a super-fast plane called the Concorde. However, the Concorde was very expensive and as a result the flights were stopped by 2003.

J: Yes, I flew on one back in 1999, a long time ago now! Thank you so much for coming in today Kate. Coming up next on the show …

UNIT 8

8.4 Lesson 8.5, Listening, Exercise B
F = Father D = Daughter

F: I've just come back from the town center. I can't believe how much graffiti there is. Especially compared to a few years ago.

D: Yes, it has really changed around there, but when you say graffiti, do you mean the street art around the mall?

F: Graffiti … street art … it's all the same thing. It looks horrible.

D: Oh, come on, Dad, those paintings were created by young local artists who won a competition. Some of it's amazing. It makes the mall look so much better.

F: Hmmm, maybe … I'd prefer nice clean white walls though.

D: But a lot of people think it's colorful and it gives young artists a space to show off their work.

F: Graffiti is not just on the walls of the mall. It's on stores, on the sides of houses and all over the bus stops. It costs a lot of money to keep cleaning it off.

D: I agree, although that's not the same thing. That's just tagging … you know, spray painting your name.

F: It's all the same thing to me.

D: What about artists like Banksy?

F: Well … his work is engaging and, another important difference, extremely valuable. People will pay a lot of money to buy his work.

8.5 Lesson 8.5, Functional Language, Exercise A

1 A: The gig has been canceled.
B: Oh no, you're kidding! I was really looking forward to it.

2 A: The tickets cost $100 each.
B: For real? You must have more money than sense.

3 A: Look, that's Chris Martin over by the bar.
B: No way! He's just someone who looks like him.

4 A: I love this song they're playing.
B: Yeah, me too. It's so catchy.

5 A: This song's number 1 right now.
B: I don't believe it. It's terrible.

UNIT 9

9.6 Lesson 9.5, Listening, Exercise B
P = Presenter H = Holly Burns

P: Many well-known stores are having a hard time. The main reason is online shopping. On today's show, is Holly Burns, who is going to tell us what can be done to get people to come into your store. Good morning Holly, welcome to the show.

H: Thank you, Jack. Yes, it's true that more and more people are using apps and sites to buy what they need. This change happened very quickly and took store owners … also known as retailers … by surprise. So they had to rethink their businesses and fight back.

P: I guess they have had to focus on what they offer that websites can't.

H: Yes, absolutely and the first advantage is face-to-face service. Online retailers are very lucky in that they have larger audiences and fewer expenses like rent or electricity, but they can't meet customers in person. In stores, real people can smile and talk with customers.

P: Yes, but a lot of people feel that when sales clerks start talking, they are just trying to get them to spend money.

H: I don't really agree; customers are frequently looking for advice. They might need to go home to think about it before spending money. So even if the customer doesn't buy something that day, they might come back in the future.

P: And they'll tell their friends about the nice people who run that store. Now, personally, when I'm shopping, I want to see what products look and feel like. If I'm buying clothes, I want to try them on.

H: Yes, that's another advantage of main street stores. While many online sites now provide detailed information about sizes and measurements, it's not the same as actually picking something up or trying it on in front of a mirror.

P: And while customers are getting hands-on with the product, the sales clerk can engage them in conversation.

H: Absolutely. Now, another advantage that real stores can use, if they are in a small town, is supporting charity soccer games or fun runs in the area. It's great publicity and should bring in new customers.

P: And on the subject of publicity, should stores advertise online?

H: Yes, of course. Just because a business doesn't sell products online doesn't mean it can't use social media to attract new customers. Posting good reviews of your products and services will also really help.

P: Well thank you, Holly. There's plenty for retailers to think about …

9.7 Lesson 9.5, Functional Language
SP = Sales Person
C1 = Customer 1 C2 = Customer 2

1 SP: Can I help you?
C1: Yes, I'm looking for accessories – something for my wife's birthday.
SP: What kind of thing are you looking for – gloves, a belt, some jewelry?
C1: Gloves are a good idea.
SP: The gloves are over there, sir. Let me know if you need help.
C1: I like these. I'll take them.

SP: Very well, sir. That's $25. How would you like to pay?

C1: By card, here.

SP: OK, if you could enter your PIN when you're ready.

C1: OK.

SP: Thank you, sir. Would you like them gift-wrapped?

C1: No, don't worry, I'll do that when I get home.

2 C2: Hello, I bought this T-shirt yesterday but it's the wrong size. It's a little big.

SP: Would you like to exchange it for a smaller one?

C2: Actually, I'd prefer to have a refund if that's OK. I'm not sure I like it that much.

SP: OK, I can do that if you have the receipt.

C2: Yes, here it is. Thanks so much for that.

UNIT 10

10.5 Lesson 10.5, Listening, Exercise B

W = Wife H = Husband SP = Sales Person C = Customer Wo = Woman

1 W: I just don't think we need one.

H: We could use it to heat up food from the night before. You can cook a meal to last a couple of evenings.

W: I don't want to eat the same dinner two nights in a row. Anyway, if you want to heat up food, you can do it in the oven.

H: Not in three minutes! It takes ten times as long in the oven. They're great for heating a meal back up if it goes cold … I mean if you're called away to answer the phone or something.

W: I don't answer the phone when I'm eating.

H: Oh come on. Everyone has one.

W: I just think they make people lazy about preparing meals. I don't want to do that. Anyway I'm pretty sure they aren't good for your health.

2 SP: Can I help you or are you just looking?

C: Well, both really. I'm looking for now but it's very likely we'll get my mother one of these soon. She's finding it more and more difficult to walk and she needs to get out and about.

SP: Well, yes, of course. That's what these are for. They give people some independence.

C: And is the price on this one typical? I mean 4,000 dollars is a lot.

SP: This is probably the best vehicle we have. It has a top speed of twelve kilometers per hour.

C: Hm, that's really fast, isn't it? My mother was never a very confident driver. I don't think it's the one for her.

3 Wo: Hello, hello, hi, is that Marion? Look, we really love the apartment but it's very hot. We have all the windows open but … Yes, we knew there was no air-conditioning, but we expected something to keep the place a little cooler. … I mean the temperature's 36 today. No, there isn't one at all. We've checked all the rooms and all the cupboards. OK, that would be very helpful. Do you think you could bring one fan for the living room and one for the bedroom? OK, I guess one will have to be enough. We'll take it down to the bedroom when we go to bed. How long will it be before you can come around? Really? We wanted to go down to the beach. We don't really want to wait here all afternoon. OK, that's fine, we'll be back here by five and you can give it to us then. Great, thanks.

10.6 Lesson 10.5, Functional language

J = Jenny S = Susanna T = Tina M = Matt

1 J: Hello, Cartwright's. Jenny speaking, how can I help you?

S: Oh, hello. Is it possible to speak to Mr. Jenner, please?

J: I'm not sure. I'll just try to put you through. No, I'm afraid his line's busy. Would you like to hold?

S: Actually, I'm very busy myself. I'll call back later.

2 T: Hi … hi Matt … hi is that you?

M: Oh, hi Tina. Yes, it's me but I can't hear you very clearly. Could you speak up?

T: Can you hear me now? I'm at Grand Central …

M: Sorry, you've gone again. I'll try to call you. Hi Tina, is that better?

T: Not really, it's a terrible line. You keep breaking up.

M: Well, I'm just picking up the car. I'm in an underground parking garage. The signal isn't very good.

T: Why didn't you tell me that? Call me again when you're outside.

UNIT 11

11.3 Lesson 11.5, Listening, Exercise B

J = Jim S = Simone

J: Did I ever tell you about what happened when I was in Libya? You know, when I was working out there years ago?

S: No, I don't think so. Why? What happened?

J: On one of our days off, we drove out to a desert town with a couple of the local guys from work. They wanted to show us some sights. Anyway, we all got out of the truck and we were walking around. Suddenly, we saw this huge cloud of dust in the distance. It was a brown-yellow color. It was clearly coming our way.

S: So, what did you do?

J: The guys we were with started yelling. They told us to run back to the truck, which was about five minutes away. By this time, we could hear the wind and started to feel it, too.

S: It sounds really scary. What happened next?

J: We got about halfway back to the truck and the wind was really strong. I could feel the sand sticking to my face. It was difficult to run as fast as I wanted to. All of the other guys took off their shirts and used them to cover their faces … you know, to protect their eyes and make sure they didn't breathe in the dust. So we did the same.

S: Oh, really? So did you get back to the truck safely in the end?

J: Yes, this one guy, Ali, managed to get back to the truck and opened the doors so we could jump straight in. It was only when I was sitting back down that I realized I was covered in sand and dust – but I didn't mind, at least we were safe! None of us could stop coughing and my chest hurt. We all drank about a liter and a half of water.

11.4 Lesson 11.5, Functional Language, Exercise B

1 Did I ever tell you about what happened when I was in Libya?

2 Why? What happened?

3 It sounds really scary. What happened next?

4 Oh, really? So, did you get back to the truck safely in the end?

UNIT 12

12.5 Lesson 12.5, Listening, Exercise B

T = Tony E = Erica

E: Tony, I've been thinking. When we have the baby, should we get rid of the TV? Should we try living without one for a few years?

T: Why?

E: Because I don't want her … or him … to sit and watch it all day. I mean, when we go to your sister's house, her children just seem to sit around all day watching cartoons.

T: Oh please! Sally lets them watch a little more TV than usual when we visit because she wants to talk to us. You know how impossible it is to talk with kids running around.

E: Isn't that what kids are supposed to do … run around?

T: Yes, of course … most of the time. But a little TV doesn't hurt. Personally, I think a limited amount of TV is good for their imagination. They learn from watching TV just like they learn from reading books.

E: But they don't learn anything if they watch cartoons all day.

T: That's not true. Most shows for very small kids are educational … even the cartoons. And kids become interested in things they see their parents are watching, like soccer.

E: Well, sorry, but I disagree. Look, all I'm saying is let's have no TV while the baby's small. While its brain's developing.

T: But what about us? Won't we want to watch TV sometimes?

E: We both have laptops and we listen to the news on the radio, anyway. Do we really need a TV in the living room?

T: What about us watching TV together … when there's a good drama or something? Are we going to watch shows on separate laptops in different rooms? That'll be a great start to family life!

E: Oh, come on! Anyway, we probably won't have time to watch TV when we have a baby.

T: Oh, well, that's the benefit of having kids' channels on the TV. When we're washing clothes or making dinner, we can put the baby in front of the TV for half an hour. It's perfectly normal.

E: Now, that's my point exactly! One minute you say children learn from TV and the next you say you'll put the baby in front of it because you're busy. Parents always say their kids will only watch TV for an hour a day and then it becomes two and then three. They should sit and read with them, go out in the yard or bake a cake or something.

T: Well, yes … maybe that's a fair point.

E: So, you agree with me?

T: Well, I'm not sure about that, but let's say I'll think about it.

12.6 Lesson 12.5, Functional Language, Exercise B

1 Oh, please! Sally lets them watch a little more TV than usual when we visit because she wants to talk to us.
2 Yes, of course … most of the time.
3 That's not true. Most shows for very small kids are educational … even the cartoons.
4 Well, sorry, but I disagree.
5 Look, all I'm saying is, let's have no TV while the baby's small.
6 Now, that's my point exactly! One minute you say children learn from TV and the next you say you'll put the baby in front of it because you're busy.
7 Well, yes … maybe that's a fair point.
8 Well, I'm not sure about that, but let's say I'll think about it.

Answer key

7.1 Smile

GRAMMAR

A

1 The sun rises in the east.
2 The president of the US lives in the White House.
3 Is there an apple in the shopping bag?
4 Tom needs to buy a new phone.
5 I'd like to order a burger without fries.

B

1 The **2** an **3** the **4** a **5** The **6** the **7** the **8** a
9 the **10** – **11** the **12** a **13** – **14** –

PRONUNCIATION

A

1 3 **2** 3 **3** 2 **4** 0 **5** 2 **6** 3

VOCABULARY

A

1 anxious **2** relaxed **3** cheerful / relaxed
4 nervous / anxious **5** happy **6** glad **7** confused
8 scared

7.2 The internet and the brain

GRAMMAR

A

1 I didn't use to like vegetables but now I do.
2 James used to have blue hair when he was a teenager.
3 Did you use to play soccer together when you were kids?
4 The weather didn't use to be so cold in March.
5 Dave speaks French because he used to live in Paris.
6 Did people really use to go everywhere on horses?

B

1 ~~used to go~~ went **2** Correct **3** ~~used~~ use **4** Correct
5 ~~can~~ be able to **6** ~~used~~ use **7** Correct

PRONUNCIATION

A

1 She didn't use to like tennis.
2 How did you use to get to school?
3 Did Robert use to work with you?
4 People used to listen to the radio in the evening.
5 People used to travel by car less frequently.
6 Did your friend Monica use to have blond hair?

VOCABULARY

A

1 plane **2** cases **3** cell / phone **4** mic **5** info
6 paper **7** intro **8** lab **9** site **10** net

B

1 photographs **2** bicycle **3** examination **4** application
5 internet

7.3 Intelligence

VOCABULARY

A

1 grew up, d **2** falling out, c **3** dropped out, e
4 gave up, b **5** made up, a

B

1 d **2** e **3** c **4** f **5** a **6** b

GRAMMAR

A

1 a – **b** the **2 a** the **b** – **3 a** – **b** the
4 a the **b** – **5 a** the **b** the **6 a** the **b** the
7 a – **b** the

B

1 Correct
2 ~~the~~
3 Correct
4 ~~the~~
5 ~~the~~

PRONUNCIATION

A

The University of Bologna is **the** oldest university in **the** world. It opened in **the** year 1088 – a little earlier than **the** University of Oxford, where teaching began in 1096. In **the** Middle Ages, it was famous across Europe for **the** study of law. **The** famous poet Dante studied there.

7.4 Reading

READING

B

Physical challenges, reading at home, socializing, doing different jobs

C

1 a **2** a, d **3** c **4** d **5** b

7.5 Listening; Functional Language

LISTENING

B

(clockwise from the top) Leonardo da Vinci, Concorde, Amy Johnson, kites, the Wright brothers, Amelia Earhart

C

1 e **2** c **3** g **4** a **5** d **6** h **7** b **8** f

FUNCTIONAL LANGUAGE

A

1 called **2** use **3** made **4** think **5** forgotten
6 use **7** know

B

a clothespin **b** (shoe) polish **c** a saw / an axe

7.6 Write a survey report

WRITING

C

1 According **2** shows **3** contrast / comparison
4 contrast / comparison **5** Both **6** lowest

WRITING PRACTICE

B

Model answer

The survey asked how 18–30-year-olds in Rochester, NY, liked to spend their free time compared to over-31-year-olds. According to the survey, 60% of 18–30-year-olds enjoy socializing compared to only 30% of people over 31.
The survey also shows a big difference for watching TV shows, which was the older group's favorite free time activity with 40% of those questioned choosing this. This was a big contrast with the younger group, of which only 5% chose watching TV.
For people over 31, working out was the least popular activity with only 10% of them choosing it, though this was higher than 18–30-year-olds at 5%.
Both groups shared a similar preference for using social media, with 30% of the younger group and 20% of the older group saying this was how they enjoyed spending their free time.

8.1 Musical taste

GRAMMAR

A

1 b **2** a **3** e **4** d **5** c

B

1 ourselves **2** himself **3** herself **4** itself **5** ourselves
6 themselves

VOCABULARY

A

1 singer **2** drummer **3** keyboard player **4** band member
5 album **6** lyrics **7** tour

B

1 cover, catchy **2** stage, audience **3** microphone, live
4 gigs, show

PRONUNCIATION

A

1 strength **2** twelfth **3** sprints **4** splashed
5 screamed

8.2 Unusual art

VOCABULARY

1 gallery **2** photograph **3** still life **4** abstract
5 sculpture **6** portrait **7** landscape

PRONUNCIATION

A

1 S **2** D **3** D **4** S **5** D **6** S **7** S **8** D

GRAMMAR

A

1 to create **2** to avoid **3** to make **4** to see **5** to take
6 to become

B

1 I bought some wood to make a picture frame.
2 Jack and Sally went to Amsterdam to visit the Van Gogh Museum.
3 Zac bought his girlfriend some flowers to surprise her.
4 Small movie theaters are the best place to watch old movies.
5 We stayed up to finish our homework.

8.3 Telling stories

VOCABULARY

A

1 comedy **2** biopic **3** Western **4** horror **5** sci-fi
6 musical

B

1 biographies **2** historical **3** Fantasy **4** adventure

PRONUNCIATION

A

1 animated animation **2** adventure adventurous
3 comedy comedian **4** fantasy fantastic
5 history historical **6** musical musician
7 romance romantic **8** science scientist

GRAMMAR

A

1 'll go **2** is **3** are **4** 'll be **5** Will, go **6** find **7** drive
8 'll take **9** get **10** 'll have

B

1 Should **2** could **3** is **4** won't **5** might not

8.4 Reading

READING

A

1 at home **2** not positive **3** is still very popular

B

1 a **2** c **3** b **4** c **5** b **6** a

8.5 Listening; Functional Language

LISTENING

A

1 F **2** D **3** D **4** F **5** F **6** Both

C

1 compared to **2** but **3** though **4** although
5 another important difference

FUNCTIONAL LANGUAGE

A

1 d, kidding **2** c, real **3** a, way **4** e, too **5** b, believe

B

1 do **2** did **3** did **4** do **5** do **6** are

8.6 Write a review

WRITING

B

positive

C

1 a **2** b **3** c **4** b **5** c **6** a

D

1 tells **2** stars **3** is **4** set **5** seeing

WRITING PRACTICE

B

Model answer

Harry Potter is a series of movies based on the children's books by JK Rowling. In the third movie, *The Prisoner of Azkaban*, Harry discovers the man believed to be involved in his parents' murder has escaped from prison.

It stars Daniel Radcliffe, Emma Watson and Gary Oldman as the escaped prisoner – Sirius Black. The acting is very good, but it is the special effects that are truly magical.

For me, the movie isn't as good as the book. A lot of important details are left out. However, it is a very enjoyable movie and is definitely worth seeing.

9.1 Spending money

PRONUNCIATION

A

1 S **2** D **3** D **4** D **5** S **6** S **7** D **8** S **9** S **10** D

B

1 half **2** path **3** because **4** stand **5** laugh **6** calm

GRAMMAR

A

1 was / were
2 wouldn't have to
3 wouldn't spend
4 could
5 'd go
6 didn't have
7 wouldn't be earning / might not be earning
8 wasn't doing
9 might be

B

1 could; would; buy
2 Would; tell; saw
3 would; say; offered
4 Would; share; won
5 had; would; go

VOCABULARY

a toward
1 spend
b on
2 borrow
c from
3 lend
d to
4 pay
e for
f by
5 take
g out
6 pay
h in
7 save
i up

9.2 Getting and giving

VOCABULARY

1 b **2** f **3** h **4** c **5** e **6** a **7** g **8** d

PRONUNCIATION

A

1 peas **2** raise **3** raised **4** racer **5** bus **6** eyes
7 plays **8** sink

GRAMMAR

A

1 c, who **2** d, which / that **3** f, when **4** b, where
5 g, who **6** a, which / that **7** e, whose

B

1 where your mother and I
2 guy who lives next door
3 when most people travel
4 the city where / in which Shakespeare
5 (that / which) I'd / I would really hate

9.3 Who needs money?

GRAMMAR

1 realizing **2** shopping **3** creating **4** making
5 collecting **6** signing **7** hiring **8** Calling

VOCABULARY

A

make: a mess; a complaint; a mistake; a decision; a profit; an offer; a living

do: the shopping; some damage; me a favor; the ironing; your homework; research

B

1 do the shopping **2** made a profit **3** do your homework
4 make a mess **5** made a complaint **6** made a mistake

PRONUNCIATION

A

pleasure /ʒ/ damage /dʒ/ decision /ʒ/ region /dʒ/
average /dʒ/ orange /dʒ/ television /ʒ/ leisure /ʒ/
image /dʒ/ religion /dʒ/ massage/ʒ/ angel /dʒ/
inclusion /ʒ/

9.4 Reading

READING

B

c

C
a 3 **b** 4 **c** 1 **d** 2

D
1 means spending all your money at once
2 all the clothes you possess
3 bringing products to your home
4 compare prices in various places
5 looking at various options without buying
6 a small store that is open at the front
7 low
8 less
9 a large piece of furniture for clothes

9.5 Listening; Functional Language

LISTENING

B
c

C
1 F They're making less money.
2 T
3 F Customers frequently ask sales clerks for advice.
4 F People like to go home and think about things and go back in the future.
5 T
6 T
7 F Businesses can use social media to attract new customers.
8 F Good reviews always help.

FUNCTIONAL LANGUAGE
1 help **2** looking **3** thing **4** over **5** take **6** pay
7 enter **8** gift **9** worry **10** wrong **11** exchange
12 refund **13** receipt

9.6 Write a 'for sale' advertisement

WRITING

A
1 b **2** a **3** d **4** e **5** c

B
1966 Jaguar E-Type – only $75,000
In excellent condition with just a few small marks on the door. It has the original leather seats. It has a top speed of 150 mph. Please contact me if you have any questions.

NEARLY NEW VESPA
I'm selling for the bargain price of $2,000. It comes with two helmets. It is big enough for two people to ride. Please contact me at vespa@hub.com for further information.

C
1 original leather seats; top speed of 150 mph; big enough for two people to ride
2 only, bargain price
3 1966 E-Type
4 two helmets
5 excellent, nearly new
6 vespa@hub.com

WRITING PRACTICE

B
Model answer
LAPTOP FOR SALE
White HP laptop in good condition. Just a small scratch on the screen. It has the latest version of Windows installed. For sale for $50. Please contact Sandra at 1-800-555-0199 for more details.

10.1 Devices

VOCABULARY
1 tablet **2** drone **3** USB drive **4** e-reader **5** power bank
6 fitness tracker

GRAMMAR

A
1 faster **2** the best **3** slower **4** more quickly
5 longer **6** The worst **7** wider **8** kinder
9 less expensive **10** the most modern **11** more reliable
12 happier

B
Suggested answers
1 In picture b, the woman is older than in picture a.
2 In picture b, the man is taller than in picture a.
3 In picture b, the man's hair is longer than in picture a.
4 In picture b, the cups are bigger than in picture a.
5 In picture b, the clock is higher (on the wall) than in picture a.
6 In picture b, the flowers are more beautiful than in picture a.
7 In picture b, the chair is more comfortable than in picture a.
8 In picture b, the TV is more modern than in picture a.

PRONUNCIATION
1 1 **2** 0 **3** 2 **4** 1 **5** 0 **6** 3

10.2 It's only good when it works

VOCABULARY
1 remember **2** connect **3** clicked **4** froze **5** make
6 blocked **7** crashes **8** installs

PRONUNCIATION
1 as young as
2 as expensive as
3 as fast as
4 as many as
5 as much as
6 as difficult as

GRAMMAR

A
1 ~~better~~ good **2** ~~like~~ as **3** Correct **4** ~~safer~~ safe
5 ~~than~~ as **6** Correct **7** ~~good~~ well **8** Correct

B
1 not as safe as **2** not as big as **3** just as good at chess as
4 not as smart as **5** just as much as

10.3 The best view in the universe

GRAMMAR

A

1 need to have **2** needs to be **3** need to know
4 need to have **5** don't need to speak / understand / know

B

1 Do you need to do more exercise? **2** Does she need to learn English? **3** Do you need to see a doctor? **4** Does he need to borrow more money?

PRONUNCIATION

A

1 S **2** D **3** S **4** D **5** D **6** S **7** D **8** D

B

1 look **2** soon **3** stood **4** put **5** loose **6** could

VOCABULARY

A

1 doing **2** repairing **3** made **4** follow **5** testing
6 solve **7** looking for **8** collect **9** do

B

1 research **2** problems **3** schedule **4** data

10.4 Reading

READING

B

cell phone, streaming services, email, social media, text messaging, booking online

C

1 d **2** b **3** d, e and f **4** a **5** c

D

1 stories **2** friends **3** updating **4** benefits **5** exciting

E

1 F **2** F **3** O **4** O **5** F

10.5 Listening; Functional Language

LISTENING

A

1 mobility scooter
2 electric fan
3 microwave

B

a 3 **b** 2 **c** 1

C

Conversation 1: **1** M **2** W **3** M **4** W
Conversation 2: **5** Her mother **6** 4,000 dollars / $4,000 **7** 12 kmph **8** It's too fast
Conversation 3: **9** F **10** T **11** F **12** F **13** T

FUNCTIONAL LANGUAGE

1 possible **2** put **3** busy **4** hold **5** back **6** hear
7 up **8** gone **9** breaking **10** signal

10.6 Write a recommendation

WRITING

C

I think you should definitely buy a dishwasher; Think about getting one that isn't too expensive to use and is a reliable brand; I'd recommend getting one that is fairly powerful; I'd also suggest getting a washing machine; I'd recommend getting a fairly large one; I'd suggest getting one that's quiet; you could buy a coffee machine

WRITING PRACTICE

C

Model answer

I think you should definitely join a gym rather than buy a fitness tracker, because most gyms offer a personal trainer service. Personal trainers are fitness experts and they'll be able to show you exercises to get in shape quickly. It will also give you the motivation you need because they are very encouraging. Fitness trackers are good for monitoring how much exercise you are doing during the day, but I'm not sure how reliable they are.

You can also choose from a variety of exercise classes at the gym, which are fun and can teach you new skills. I started boxing classes last year and I absolutely love it!

11.1 Natural wonders

VOCABULARY

A

U	Y	S	F	F	I	L	C	D	D	O
L	A	N	A	C	A	N	Y	O	N	C
Y	E	L	L	A	V	A	J	Q	B	E
A	L	I	G	H	T	S	L	N	A	A
M	O	U	N	T	A	I	N	H	Y	N
R	A	I	N	F	O	R	E	S	T	S
L	E	E	H	A	R	B	O	R	R	F
N	V	O	N	A	C	L	O	V	K	E
W	A	T	E	R	F	A	L	L	T	E
U	C	L	S	T	R	E	S	E	D	R

B

Land: volcano; rainforest; desert; canyon; cliffs; valley; cave; mountain
Water: harbor; bay; waterfall; reef; ocean; canal
Others: lights

PRONUNCIATION

1 meat **2** best **3** feed **4** feel **5** men **6** check
7 said **8** clever

GRAMMAR

A

1 is located **2** was eroded **3** is made **4** are attracted
5 be reached **6** covered **7** is known

B

1 is described
2 impresses
3 are designed
4 gives
5 is reflected
6 create
7 was built
8 died
9 was filled

11.2 Animal images

VOCABULARY

Mammals: bear; elephant; gorilla; lion; monkey; panda; tiger
Birds: eagle; duck; owl; parrot; penguin
Insects: ant; bee; butterfly; fly; mosquito; moth
Reptiles: alligator; crocodile; lizard; snake
Amphibians: frog; toad
Fish: shark; tuna

GRAMMAR

1 easy **a** to get **2** disappointed **b** to hear
3 impossible / dangerous **c** to drive **4** dangerous **d** to go
5 lucky **e** to see

PRONUNCIATION

1 5 **2** 7 **3** 7 **4** 6 **5** 6 **6** 6 **7** 8 **8** 8

11.3 Throw-away world

PRONUNCIATION

A

cloud √; fail √; laugh √; trail √; plastic √; family √;
reptile √; lake √; climate √; left √

GRAMMAR

A

1 ~~Even we~~ We even
2 ~~The monkeys even~~ Even the monkeys
3 Correct
4 ~~My grandmother was even~~ Even my grandmother
5 ~~have even~~ even have
6 Correct
7 ~~The most remote places on Earth even~~ Even the most remote…
8 Correct

B

1 even the locals **2** don't even use **3** don't even like
4 even my little sister **5** He even eats burgers

VOCABULARY

A

1 everywhere **2** somewhere **3** Nowhere **4** Anywhere
5 somewhere **6** everywhere **7** Nowhere

B

1 my glasses anywhere **2** Japanese restaurants everywhere
3 somewhere really nice **4** nowhere to park **5** everywhere you look **6** anywhere to stay

11.4 Reading

READING

B

1 Niagara Falls is in the US and Canada.
2 It is 53 meters high.
3 Over 30 million people visit it per year.

C

1 It is a magnificent natural wonder.
2 It is not as impressive.
3 It hasn't changed too much over the years.
4 A huge number of tourists mean that there is money to be made.
5 No one really seemed to be appreciating the amazing natural beauty.

11.5 Listening; Functional Language

LISTENING

B

1 a desert in Libya **2** a sandstorm

C

1 F; he was driven to a desert town to see some sights
2 T **3** T **4** T **5** F; to protect their eyes and to make sure they didn't breathe in the dust **6** F; he noticed he was dusty

FUNCTIONAL LANGUAGE

A

1 ever **2** happened **3** sounds; next **4** really; end

11.6 Write an email giving suggestions and advice

WRITING

C

1 were **2** idea **3** sure **4** must **5** should

D

1 ought to / should
2 recommend speaking
3 must visit / ought to visit
4 suggest you take / suggest taking

WRITING PRACTICE

B

Model answer

Hi Matthew,
Sorry to hear you are feeling so nervous about starting your new job. To be honest, though, it is completely normal to feel that way.
First of all, try to appear confident and friendly. Make sure you introduce yourself to everyone and try to remember their names.

Second, if I were you, I'd make sure I arrived at least ten minutes early for the first few weeks. This will give your boss the impression that you are reliable and hard-working.
Finally, go to any company networking events. They are a good way to make connections and to find out more about the company.
I hope that helps.
Good luck!
James

12.1 The news

VOCABULARY

A

1 get the news
2 follow the news
3 report the news
4 breaking news
5 journalist
6 share news stories
7 news headlines

B

1 follow the news; news headlines
2 gets the news; shares news stories
3 journalists; report the news
4 breaking news

GRAMMAR

A

1 she loved posting photos of herself
2 if / whether Bill knew the way to the movie theater
3 her that she'd / would see her the next day
4 if / whether he should hand in his homework then
5 Daniel was watching the soccer game that night

B

1 Correct
2 Correct
3 Lionel told me that he couldn't answer my question.
4 James told us that he didn't like sports much.
5 Samantha told me she was forty-two a couple of months ago.

PRONUNCIATION

A

1 S **2** D **3** S **4** D **5** D **6** D **7** S **8** S **9** D **10** D

B

1 what **2** comb **3** bored **4** clothes **5** clock **6** cloth

12.2 On the box

VOCABULARY

1 channels **2** season finale **3** season **4** stream
5 series / show **6** episode **7** box set
8 show / series

PRONUNCIATION

A

1 you'd lost **2** the movie had started **3** I heard about it
4 we'd found it **5** they played well **6** mom had cooked

GRAMMAR

A

1 was; hadn't eaten
2 did not / didn't understand, had missed
3 had (already) started, arrived
4 recognized, had taught
5 thanked, had given
6 had (never) tasted, was
7 was, had not taken / hadn't taken
8 couldn't, had left

B

1 Mohammed **2** Yumi **3** Jason **4** Leo

12.3 Advertising

GRAMMAR

A

1 Should **2** Should **3** 'll **4** 'll **5** should **6** Will **7** 'll
8 Should

B

1 Should we go **2** Will you help **3** Tina will pass
4 should we invite

VOCABULARY

1 grab your attention **2** message **3** brand **4** slogan
5 catch your eye **6** connect with **7** logo

PRONUNCIATION

1 bad **2** head **3** man **4** sand **5** said **6** dad **7** merry
8 guess

12.4 Reading

READING

B

1 Weather **2** Lifestyle **3** Entertainment **4** Education
5 News Headlines **6** Travel **7** Sports **8** Finance

C

1 fairly good **2** gossip **3** health **4** boxing **5** bad news

D

1 It will be 24 degrees tomorrow.
2 10% of UK parents help children with their school work.
3 60% of Indian parents help children with their school work.
4 Herito was knocked down in the ninth round.
5 Hemmings has won all three of his fights this year.
6 AbbeyWide lost $28 million in 2017.

12.5 Listening; Functional Language

LISTENING

B

1 Because they are going to have a baby.

C

1 E **2** T **3** E **4** T **5** E **6** T **7** T **8** E **9** E

FUNCTIONAL LANGUAGE

A

1 please **2** course **3** true **4** disagree **5** saying
6 exactly **7** fair **8** sure

12.6 Write a story

WRITING

A

1 The story is *Cinderella*.
2 It is written as a news report and not as a conventional fairy tale. Only part of the story is reported.

B

1 disappeared
2 had received
3 were dancing
4 had seen
5 didn't take
6 hadn't seen
7 had fallen
8 rushed
9 chased
10 had dropped

C

Reported speech:
One man said she was the prettiest girl he had ever seen.
The prince's aunt told us that she hadn't seen her nephew so happy for many years and that he had clearly fallen madly in love.
He told us he would search the entire kingdom and that he would not stop until they were reunited.
Direct speech:
'If I have to try the slipper on the foot of every girl in the land, then I will do it', he said.

WRITING PRACTICE

B

Model answer

Terrified Girl Escapes House of Bears
A young girl known as Goldilocks shares her story of escape.
Goldilocks had been walking through the woods on her way home when she saw a cottage with its door wide open.
'I thought I had better check it hadn't been robbed,' she told us. So she went inside. No one was there. On the table were three bowls of delicious porridge. She didn't want the food to go to waste and she was feeling very hungry. She tried all three bowls. The first was too hot, the second was too cold, but the third bowl was just right.
After eating, she felt tired. She went upstairs and fell asleep. Suddenly she heard a growling noise and woke up to find herself surrounded by three bears. She screamed and pushed past the smallest bear. Then she ran down the stairs and out of the house as fast she could.

Notes